MY FIRST PIANO
Adventure®

FOR THE YOUNG BEGINNER
by Nancy and Randall Faber

Hello! I'm Tap, the music firefly.
Look for me throughout the book!

This book belongs to:

Progress Chart

FF161

Friends at the Piano

1. Can you name 3 or 4 of your friends?
2. Guess what? Now you have 6 more friends.
   Point to us and say our names with your teacher.

Katie

Carlos

Dallas

Marta
and
Millie
the twins

Mrs. Razzle-Dazzle
the piano teacher

Roll Call  ①

Steady Beat

Tap a steady beat on your lap as you listen to the CD.
*Enjoy learning the words and singing along!**

Sing

Friends at the piano, we're a band of friends!
Meet Millie, meet Marta, they're the twins.
Hey, Carlos. Hey, Dallas. Katie, too.
Mrs. Razzle-Dazzle is tapping with you.

Chant and tap the beat

Tap the beat! Roll Call, please!

Millie 2 3 4 5 6 7 8,
Marta 2 3 4 5 6 7 8,
Carlos 2 3 4, Dallas 2 3 4,
Katie 2 3 4, Mrs. Raz-zle-Daz-zle,
Raz-zle, Raz-zle-Daz-zle.

Drum roll with hands

Drum roll now for you, Yea!
Friends at the piano!

Paste your picture here.

*Teacher Note: Students may take several weeks to learn the words and name of each "friend."

The "I'm Great" Pose
Posture at the Piano

Carlos

Marta

Millie

1. Sit **STRAIGHT** and **TALL** on the front part of the bench.

2. With arms straight, your knuckles should touch the **FALLBOARD**. If you have to lean, move the bench forward or backward.

Dallas

1 2 3 4 5 6 7 8 9 10 !

Katie

3. Silently place your hands in a loose fist on the **KEYS**. Your arms should be level with the keyboard. If not, you may need to sit on a cushion. Is your back still straight?

This is your **I'M GREAT POSE!**

4. Try the I'm Great Trick!

Balance a small stuffed animal on your head. Can you keep your great **POSTURE** while your teacher counts to 10?

Sounds on the Piano

Exploring the Keyboard

1. Play some **WHITE KEYS** all over the piano keyboard.

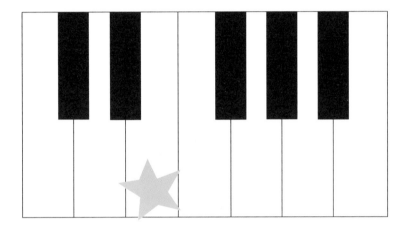

2. Find the **BLACK KEYS** and play some all over the piano keyboard.

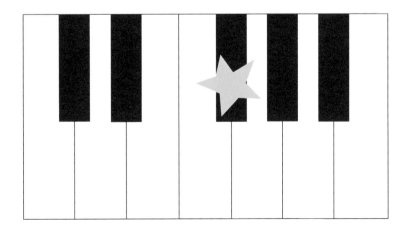

3. Find the **FALLBOARD** and create knocking sounds with loose fists. Then tap the **PIANO BENCH.**

Can you knock and chant your name?

4. Create some **SOFT** sounds anywhere on the keyboard.

5. Create some **LOUD** sounds anywhere on the keyboard.

6. Create some very **SHORT** sounds on the piano. Bounce your fingers quickly off the keys!

7. Create some very **LONG** sounds on the piano. Hold the keys down until the sound has completely faded away. Time it with a second-hand watch!

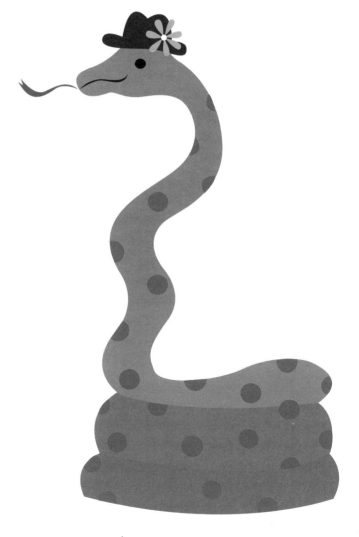

♩ Can you find Tap?

Will You Play?

Improvising with a Duet

soft | loud | long | short

1. Your teacher will play a musical question. Create the answer by making sounds together at the piano.

2. Circle a character at the bottom of the page each time you play this song. Can you find Tap?

Teacher Duet:

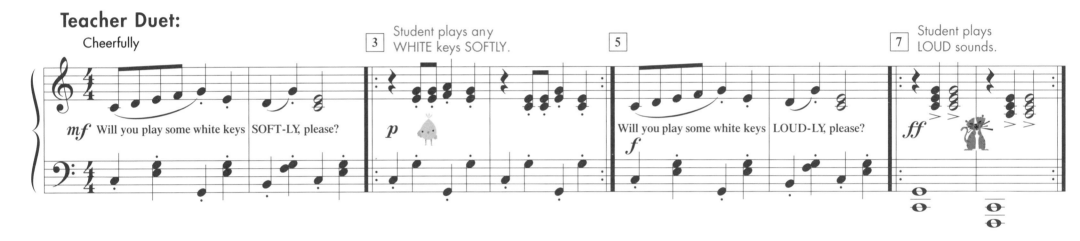

Cheerfully

mf Will you play some white keys SOFT-LY, please?

3 Student plays any WHITE keys SOFTLY.

p

5

Will you play some white keys LOUD-LY, please?

f

7 Student plays LOUD sounds.

ff

9

mf Will you tap the pia-no bench now with me?

11 Student and teacher TAP the piano BENCH.

13

Will you tap the fall-board now with me?

15 Student and teacher TAP the FALLBOARD.

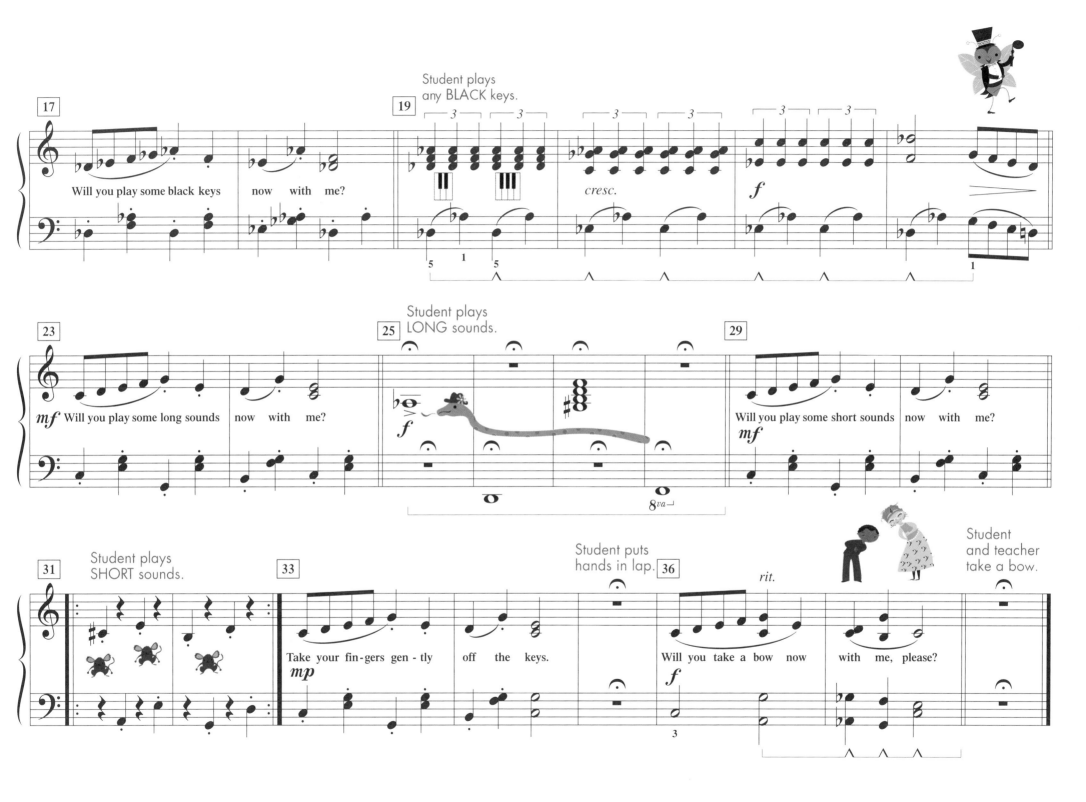

Stone on the Mountain

Technique: Arm Weight and Round Hand Shape

1. Pretend you have beautiful round stones in your hands. Katie's stone is red. What color is your stone?

2. Learn the words and do the motions for this song with your teacher. Can you chant with the voices on the CD?

3. Your teacher will demonstrate one of the pictures. Point to the one that matches. Then you be the teacher!

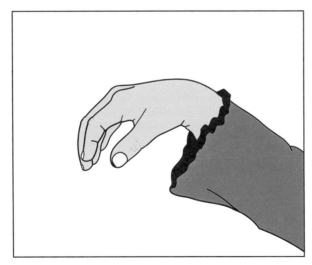

Stone on the mountain

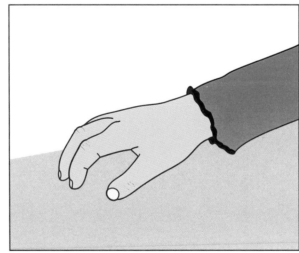

falls to the ground.
(Let the weight of your arm drop freely into your lap.)

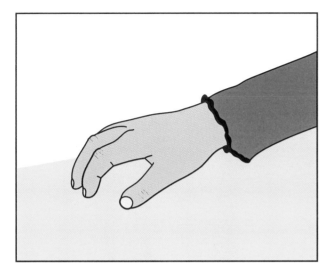

Hold it, mold it,

roll it around.

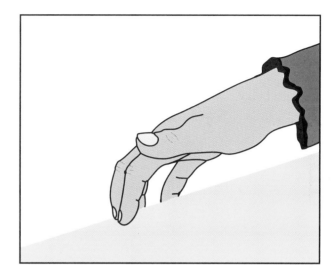

Lift your thumb, tap 1-2-3.

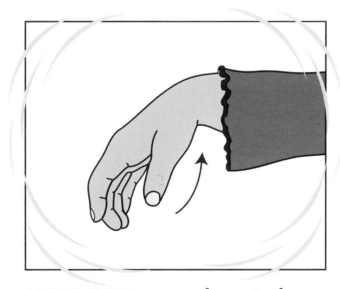

WHOOSH! goes the wind

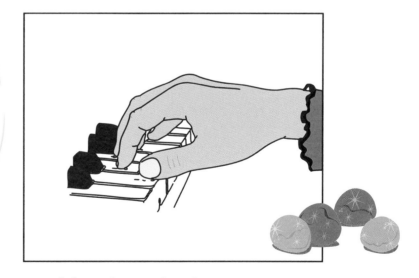

and land on the keys.

Check yourself: Are you still holding your stone?
Is your hand rounded, resting gently on the keys?

Left Hand and Right Hand
Exploring Finger Numbers

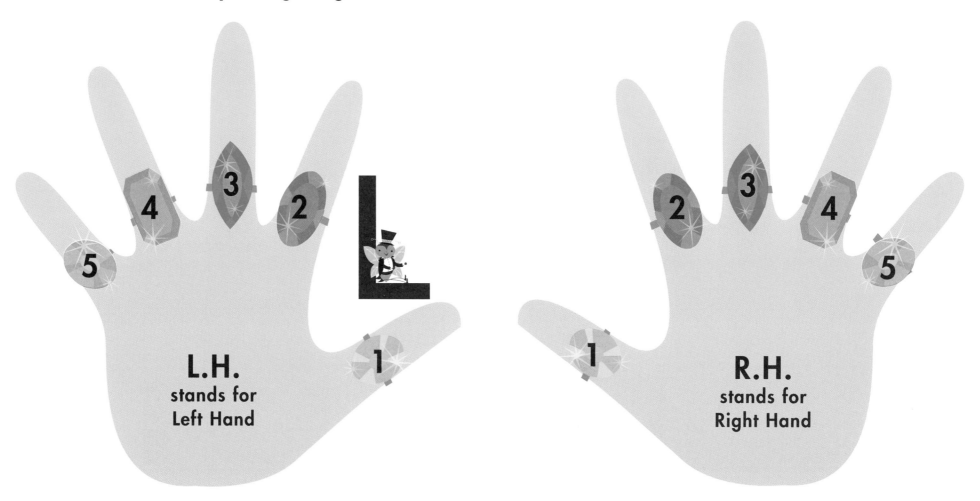

L.H.
stands for
Left Hand

R.H.
stands for
Right Hand

Tips from Tap:

1. Can you fit your hands over these hands? Can you find the **L** of the left hand?

2. Your teacher will sing, "*Mary had a little lamb, little lamb, little lamb. Mary had a little lamb, she pet it with her **LEFT** hand (or **RIGHT**).*" Quickly put your hand over the one sung. Repeat!

3. Wave "hi" to Tap with fingers **1, 2, 3, 4,** and **5**.

4. Sing and do finger motions for *This Old Man* with the CD. 4

FF1619

Cookie Dough

Technique: Firm Fingertips

Teacher Note: Student may also use clay or a sponge for "dough."

1. Use a **round hand position** on a **tabletop**. Pretend you are pressing chocolate chips into cookie dough!

2. Learn the rhyme with your teacher and the CD. Gently tap the dough 4 times with each fingertip. Use **R.H.**, then **L.H.**

Balance 1 on its side tip.
Press that little chocolate chip.

one, one, one, one

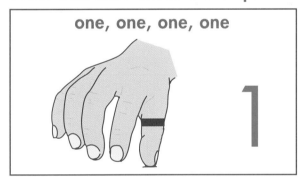

Balance 2 on fingertip.
Press that little chocolate chip.

two, two, two, two

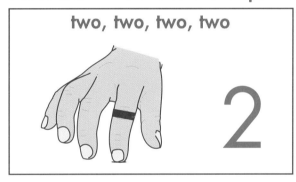

Balance 3 on fingertip.
Press that little chocolate chip.

three, three, three, three

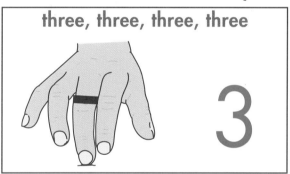

Balance 4 on fingertip.
Press that little chocolate chip.

four, four, four, four

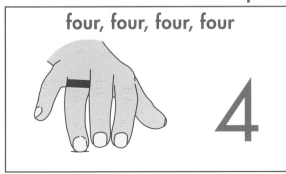

Balance 5 on fingertip.
Press that little chocolate chip.

five, five, five, five

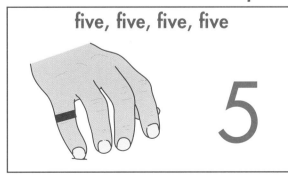

Make a round donut shape with fingers 1 and 3.

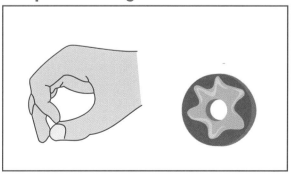

Teacher Note: Student will put thumb behind finger 3.

Dallas Dips L.H. Donuts
Sounds Going Lower on White Keys

When you play the low keys,
the sounds are lower!

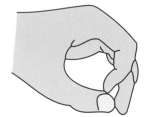

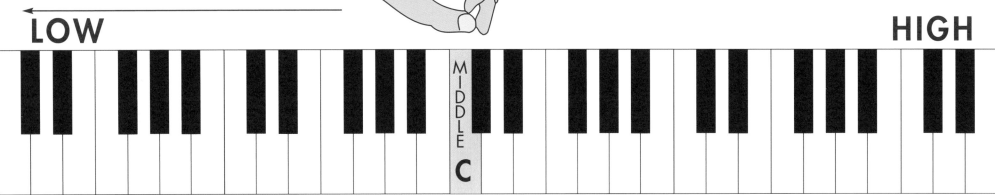

LOW ← MIDDLE C → HIGH

1. In the air with your teacher:

Pretend to dip a **L.H. 3-1 donut** in milk by dipping from your wrist. Say, "Dip, dip, dip, dip."

2. On the keyboard:

Start on MIDDLE C using a **L.H. 3-1 donut**. Play all the white keys going LOWER—to the left. Think, "Dip, dip, dip," etc. as you play.

3. Circle a donut each day you "dip your donuts" this week.

Dallas Dips R.H. Donuts

Sounds Going Higher on White Keys

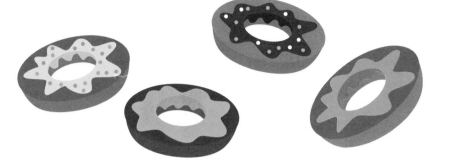

When you play the high keys, the sounds are higher!

LOW  **HIGH**

MIDDLE C

1. In the air with your teacher:

Pretend to dip a **R.H. 3-1 donut** in milk by dipping from your wrist. Say, "Dip, dip, dip, dip."

2. On the keyboard:

Start on MIDDLE C using a **R.H. 3-1 donut**. Play all the white keys going HIGHER—to the right. Then play, keeping a steady beat with the teacher duet or CD!

Teacher Duet: (Student begins on Middle C.)

⑦ Twinkle, Twinkle Little Star

Tips from Millie and Marta:

1. First, sing and point to the stars on the page.

2. Next, rest your **R.H. 3-1 donut** on top of your teacher's hand as she/he plays the song using finger 3.

3. Now play with **R.H.**, then **L.H.** You may learn just the first page this week.

Repeated Notes

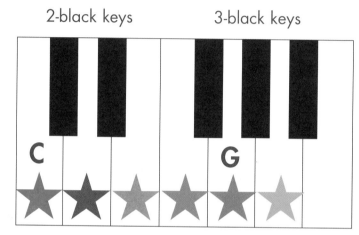

2-black keys   3-black keys

C   G

Note: A colorful paper wad, etc. may be placed on C and G to locate the first two pitches.

lit - tle

twin - kle   star.

How I

won - der

what you

Twin - kle,

are.

FF1619

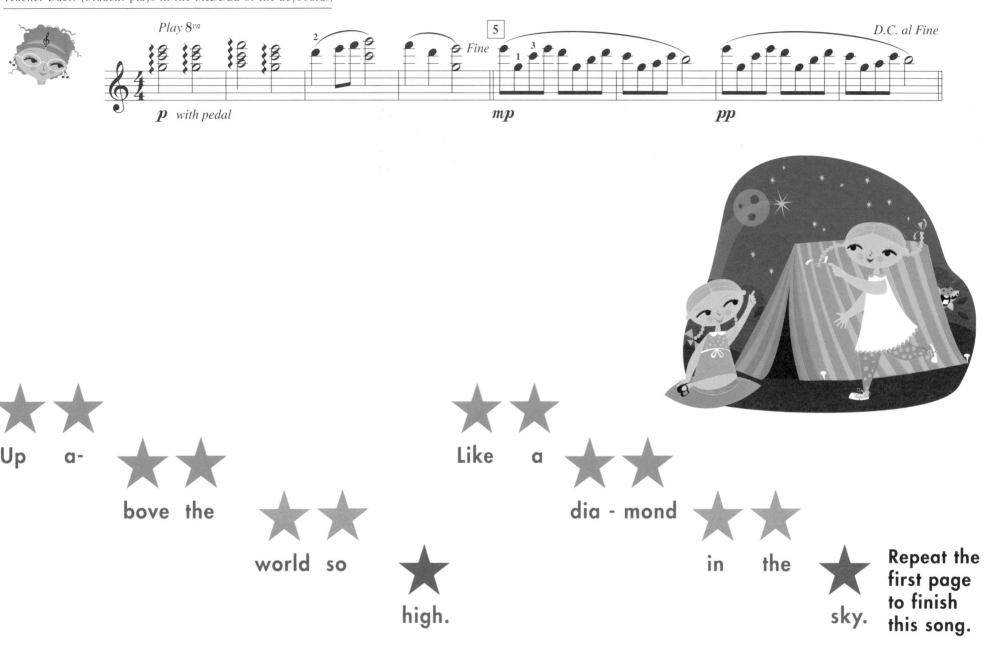

Up a-

bove the

world so

high.

Like a

dia - mond

in the

sky.

Repeat the first page to finish this song.

4. Exercise your fingers with *What's in the Honey Pot?* from the Writing Book, pp. 12–13.

8

Black-Key Groups
Two and Three Black Keys

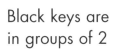

Black keys are
in groups of 2

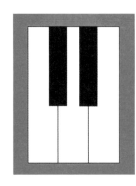

and 3.

1. Play and count all the **2-black-key groups**
on the piano. How many are there?

   Circle the friend with the correct number.

Millie   Marta   Dallas

2. Play and count all the **3-black-key groups**
on the piano. How many are there?

   Circle the friend with the correct number.

Mrs. Razzle-Dazzle   Carlos   Katie

FF1619

Monster Bus Driver

Imitating Rhythms on Black Keys

1. On any 2-black-keys:

Imitate the horn sounds your teacher plays. Use L.H. or R.H. **fingers 2-3**.

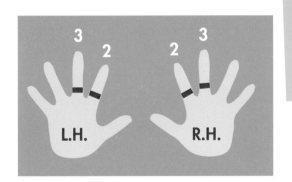

2. On any 3-black-keys:

Imitate the horn sounds your teacher plays. Use L.H. or R.H. **fingers 2-3-4**.

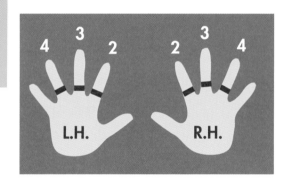

♩ Can you find Tap?

Teacher plays black-key rhythms for students to imitate. (Student plays 1 octave LOWER or HIGHER than the teacher.)

1a.   1b. 1c.  1d. 1e.

2a.   2b. 2c.   2d. 2e.

Wrist, Forearm, Fingertips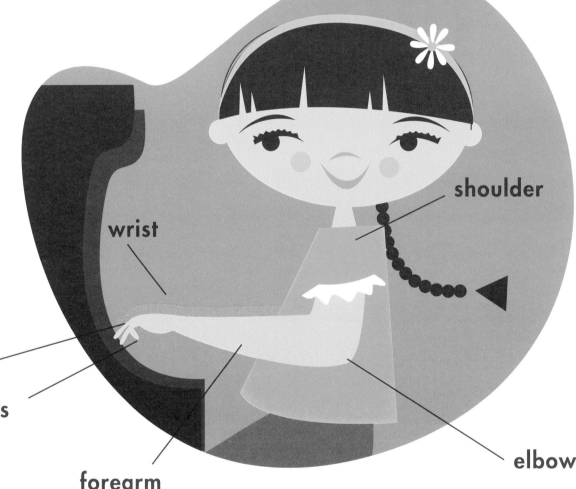

Technique: Introducing the Arm

1. Listen to your teacher sing the song (or use the CD).
   Point to the different parts of your body.

2. Play a steady beat on the **second to lowest white key**
   while your teacher plays the melody.
   Keep a great steady beat!

Wrist, forearm, fingertips—fingertips!
Wrist, forearm, fingertips,
I know how to find my
Knuckles, elbow, shoulder, too.
Wrist, forearm, fingertips—fingertips!

shoulder

wrist

knuckles

fingertips

elbow

forearm

Teacher melody for *Wrist, Forearm, Fingertips:*

Wrist, fore-arm, fin-ger-tips, fin-ger-tips. Wrist, fore-arm, fin-ger-tips, I know how to find my knuck-les, el-bow, shoul-der, too. Wrist, fore-arm, fin-ger-tips, fin-ger-tips!

FF1619

Mitsy's Cat Back
Technique: Flexible Wrist

Teacher Note: These wrist motions serve as preparation for the rainbow wrist gestures shown on the next pages.

1. Mrs. Razzle-Dazzle has a cat named Mitsy.
   Arch your **R.H.** wrist like Mitsy the cat arches her back.
   Repeat with **L.H.**

2. On the **closed piano lid**, do the motions for this song with your teacher. Can you sing with the CD?

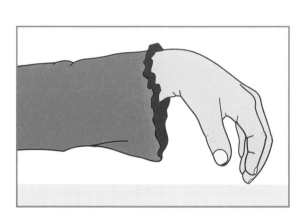

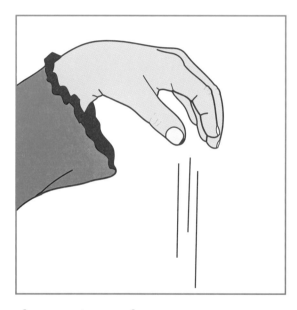

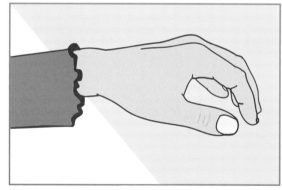

Do a cat back, do a cat back,

do a LEAP and

land upon your fingertips!
(Repeat all motions as the melody continues.)

Teacher melody for *Mitsy's Cat Back:*

Tips from Mitsy:

1. Point to each box where **L.H. fingers 2-3** play together.

2. Listen and watch your teacher play.

3. Your turn! Play and make L.H. rainbows to each LOWER **2-black-key group**. Your teacher may press the pedal as you play.

L.H. Rainbows

Technique: Graceful Wrist Motion

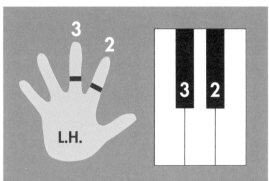

Start on the MIDDLE 2-black-keys.

L.H.

play together | 2 | 3 |

Say: Rainbow

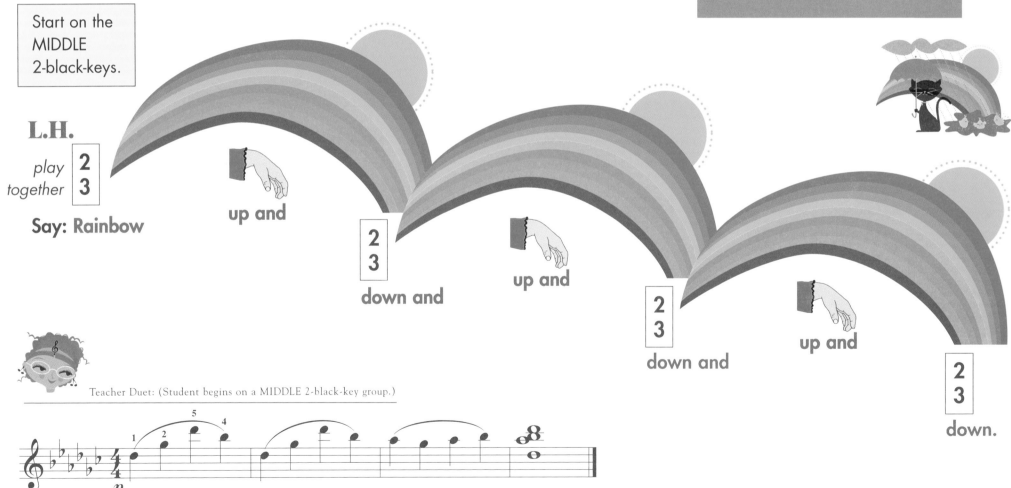

up and

| 2 | 3 |

down and

up and

| 2 | 3 |

down and

up and

| 2 | 3 |

down.

Teacher Duet: (Student begins on a MIDDLE 2-black-key group.)

Chant: *Rain - bow   up   and   down   and   up   and   down   and   up   and   down.*

R.H. Rainbows

Technique: Graceful Wrist Motion

Tips from Tap:

1. Point to each box where **R.H. fingers 2-3** play together.

2. Listen and watch your teacher play.

3. Your turn! Play and make R.H. rainbows to each HIGHER **2-black-key group**. Your teacher may press the pedal as you play.

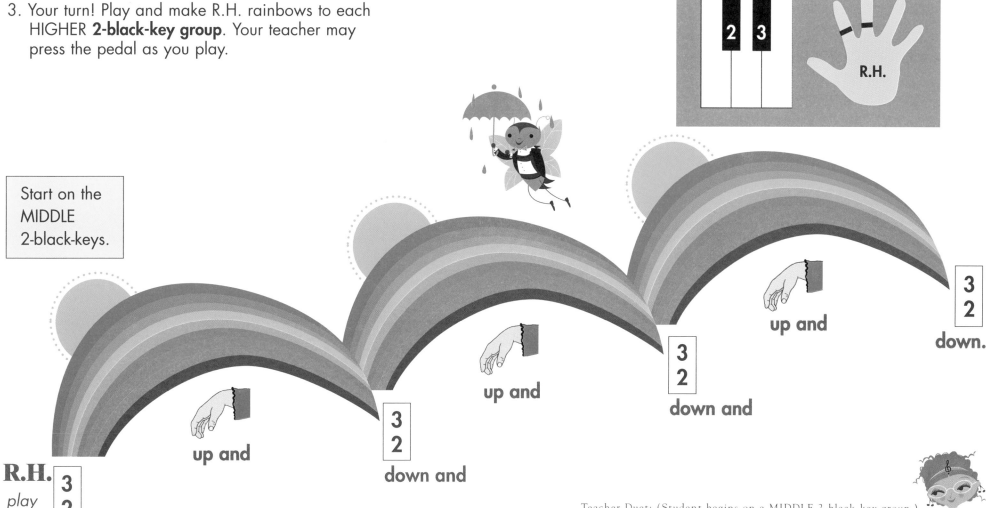

Start on the MIDDLE 2-black-keys.

R.H. *play together*

3
2

Rainbow

up and

3
2

down and

up and

3
2

down and

up and

3
2

down.

Teacher Duet: (Student begins on a MIDDLE 2-black-key group.)

Chant: *Rain - bow   up   and   down   and   up   and   down   and   up   and   down.*

⑭ Kangaroo Show

Playing L.H. Fingers 2-3

Tips from the Kangaroo:

1. Be the teacher! With L.H. finger 2, point to the numbers and say, **"2-2-2, together,"** etc.

2. Listen and watch your teacher play.

3. Your turn! Play and make kangaroo leaps to each LOWER **2-black-key group**.

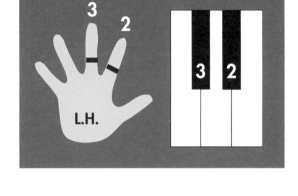

Start on the MIDDLE 2-black-keys.

play together

BOING!

L.H. 2   2   2 | 2 / 3 |

Kan-ga-roo show,

Move DOWN to next *lower* group.

BOING!

2   2   2 | 2 / 3 |

look at them go!

BOING!

2   2   2 | 2 / 3 |

Hop-ping so low,

BOING!

| 2 / 3 |

BOING!

15 Katie Scores!

Playing R.H. Fingers 2-3

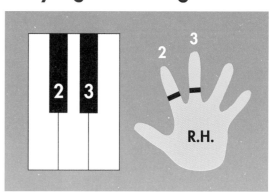

Tips from Katie:

1. Be the teacher! With R.H. finger 2, point to the numbers and say, **"2-2-2, together,"** etc.

2. Listen and watch your teacher play.

3. Your turn! Play and make the soccer ball fly to each HIGHER **2-black-key group**.

3
2

YEA!

2 2 2 | 3
2

we scored a goal,

Move UP to next higher group.

2 2 2 | 3
2

kick it so high;

Start on the MIDDLE 2-black-keysl.

play together

R.H. 2 2 2 | 3
2

Soc-cer ball fly,

Tigers at My Door

Forte and Piano with Scale Steps

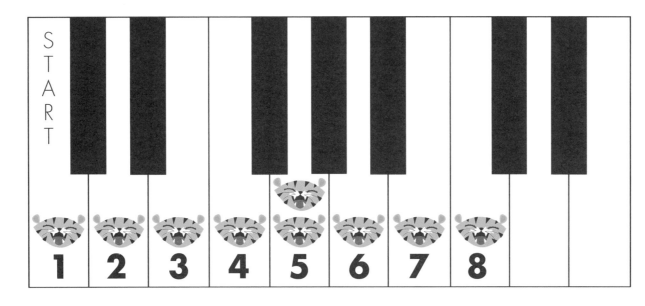

Teacher Note: A colorful paper wad, etc. may locate the opening C key. Two items may mark the G key.

f **(forte)** means LOUD

p **(piano)** means SOFT

Tips from the Tigers:

1. Circle *f* or *p* for the animal sounds on the next page.

2. Use a 2-1 donut and play the TIGER KEYS on the piano with the Teacher Duet or CD. Your teacher will guide you. Notice that "key 5" is played TWO times!

3. Listen for *f* and *p* sounds.

FF1619

TIGERS!

1, 2, 3, 4, 5
tigers
at my door!

5, 6, 7, 8
"Hey, let's roar and
stay up late."

f or *p*

RABBITS!

1, 2, 3, 4, 5
rabbits
at my door!

5, 6, 7, 8
"Hey, let's hop and
stay up late."

f or *p*

PUPPIES!

1, 2, 3, 4, 5
puppies
at my door!

5, 6, 7, 8
"Hey, let's bark and
stay up late."

f or *p*

SPIDERS!

1, 2, 3, 4, 5
spiders
at my door!

5, 6, 7, 8
"Hey, let's sleep.
It's getting late."

f or *p*

Teacher Duet: Repeat for "PUPPIES" and "SPIDERS" verse. Student plays 2 OCTAVES HIGHER.

f 1,   2,   3,   4,   5   ti-gers at my door!   5,   6,   7,   8   "Hey, let's roar and stay up late."

p 1,   2,   3,   4,   5   rab-bits at my door!   5,   6,   7,   8   "Hey, let's hop and stay up late."

WRITING BOOK **18-19**

Wendy the Whale

17

Playing L.H. Fingers 2-3-4

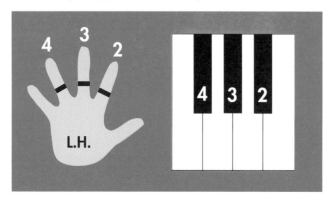

Note: The teacher may pedal
as the student plays.

Start on a
MIDDLE
3-black-key group.

*play
together*

L.H. **2**   **2**   **2**

f

2
3
4

Wen - dy   the   whale

Move DOWN to
next lower group.

2   **2**   **2**

2
3
4

moves her   big   tail

2   **2**   **2**

2
3
4

deep, down, and low.

Tips from Dallas: (pp. 30–31)

1. Be the teacher! With L.H. finger 2, point to the numbers and say, **"2-2-2, together,"** etc.

2. Listen and watch your teacher play.

3. Your turn! Pretend your hand is a whale, doing a slow leap and dive into each LOWER **3-black-key group.**

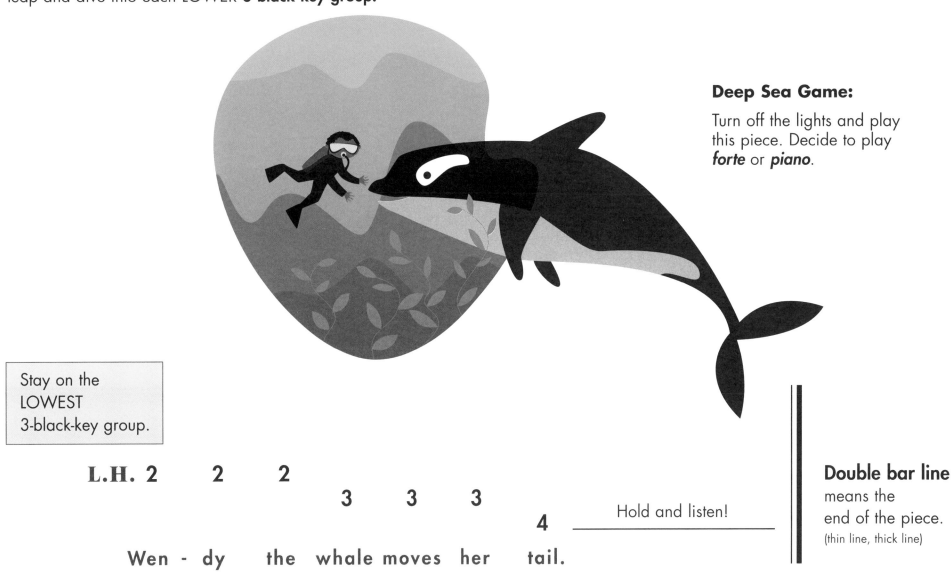

Deep Sea Game:

Turn off the lights and play this piece. Decide to play **forte** or **piano**.

Stay on the LOWEST 3-black-key group.

L.H. 2   2   2
3   3   3
4   _____ Hold and listen!

Wen - dy   the   whale moves   her   tail.

Double bar line means the end of the piece. (thin line, thick line)

Magic Tree House

Playing R.H. Fingers 2-3-4

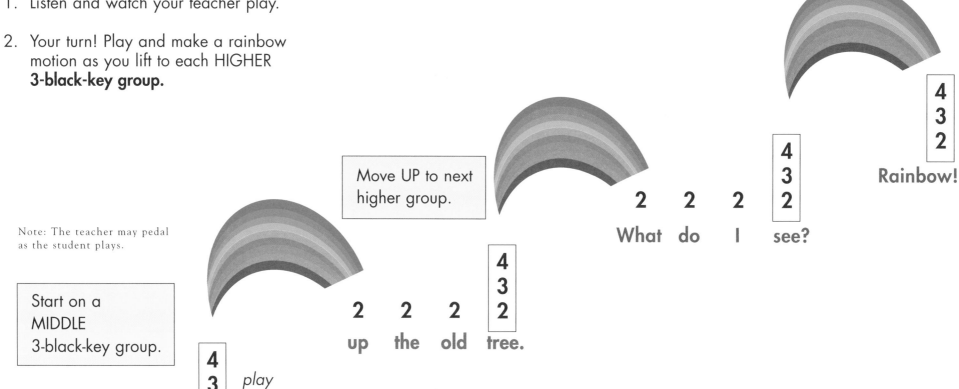

Tips from Millie and Marta:

1. Listen and watch your teacher play.

2. Your turn! Play and make a rainbow motion as you lift to each HIGHER **3-black-key group.**

Note: The teacher may pedal as the student plays.

Start on a MIDDLE 3-black-key group.

Move UP to next higher group.

R.H. **2**   **2**   **2**
f **Come climb with**
4
3
2
me, *play together*

2   **2**   **2**
4
3
2
up   the   old   tree.

2   **2**   **2**
4
3
2
What   do   I   see?

4
3
2
Rainbow!

Stay on the
HIGHEST
3-black-key group.

R.H. 2 3 4 2 3 4 2 _____ Hold and listen! _____

p Rain - bow is high in the sky.

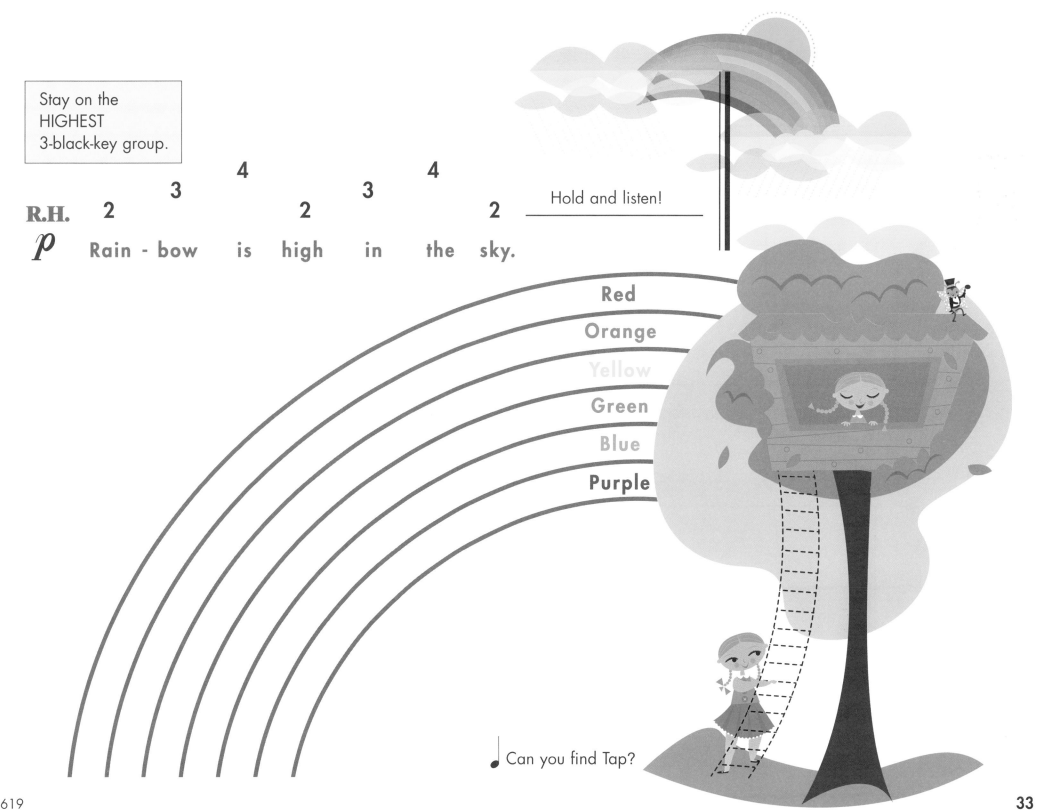

Red
Orange
Yellow
Green
Blue
Purple

♩ Can you find Tap?

Quarter Note = 1 beat

stem

head

1. Say "quarter note" in a **forte** voice, **piano** voice, high voice, low voice.

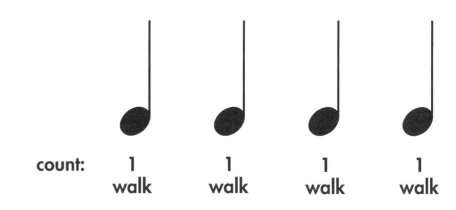

count: **1** **walk** **1** **walk** **1** **walk** **1** **walk**

2. Tap and count aloud **forte**, then **piano**.

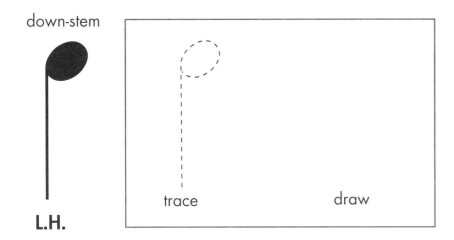

down-stem

L.H.

trace   draw

3. Trace, then draw a quarter note for the **left hand.**

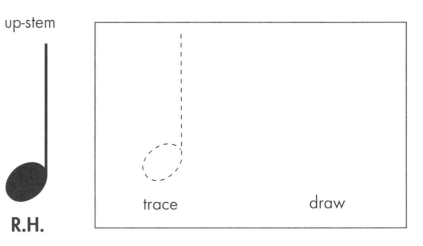

up-stem

R.H.

trace   draw

4. Trace, then draw a quarter note for the **right hand.**

Dancing Feet
Tracking the Beat

Tips from your friends:

1. Circle each group of **R.H.** notes in **RED**.
   Circle each group of **L.H.** notes in **BLUE**.

2. Play each group with the correct hand
   on any key. Use a **2-1 donut**.

Keep a steady beat!

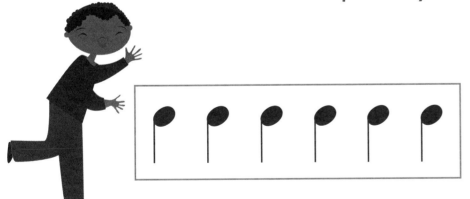

3. Your teacher will play a group of notes with the **left** or **right** hand.
   Point to the group you hear.

4. Have fun singing and tapping notes to
   Buckle My Shoe, Writing Book, pp. 22–23.

(19)

✏️ | WRITING BOOK **22-23**   **35**

Cuckoo Clock

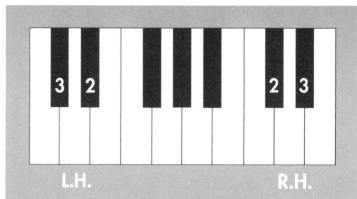

Alternating Right and Left Hand

Tips from Tap:

1. With your teacher, tap on the door, floor, and the closed piano lid, saying,

   right - right - left - left, right - left - right - left.

2. Play on the 2-black keys and say, "right - right," etc. Is your clock keeping a steady beat?

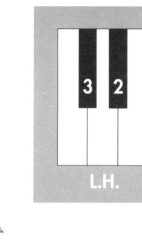

Play fingers 2 and 3 at the same time.

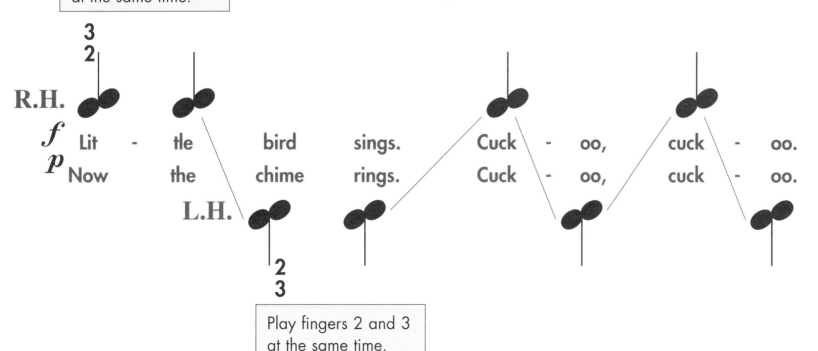

Play fingers 2 and 3 at the same time.

Repeat Sign
These dots mean to play this page once again.

R.H. f Lit - tle bird sings. Cuck - oo, cuck - oo.

p Now the bird chime rings. Cuck - oo, cuck - oo.

L.H.

Teacher Duet: (Student plays in the MIDDLE of the keyboard.)

Student continues by "chiming" the time. Teacher may depress the pedal for chimes.

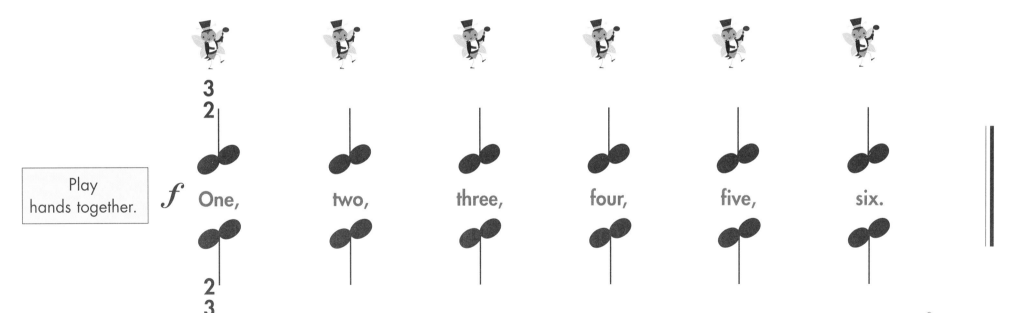

Play hands together.

𝒇 One,   two,   three,   four,   five,   six.

The Cuckoo's Secret:
Decide a number that the cuckoo will chirp: **"2 o'clock, 4 o'clock,"** etc.
Play the first page, then chime the hour you chose on the 2-black keys. Your teacher must guess the time!

Dinosaur Music Night

Quarter-Note Song on Lowest Black Keys

21

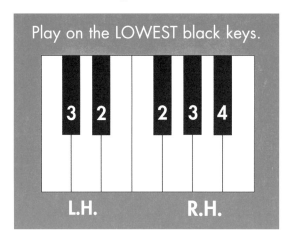

Play on the LOWEST black keys.

3 2   2 3 4

L.H.   R.H.

Words by Crystal Bowman

R.H.

f

4		3		2				
This	is	my	pet	di	-	no	-	saur;	he
loves	to	stomp	and	loud	-	ly	roar.	He
came	to	my	school's	mu	-	sic	night,	and

Play 3 times!

L.H. 2 / 3

play together

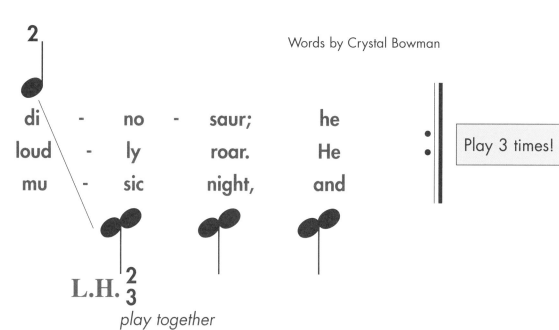

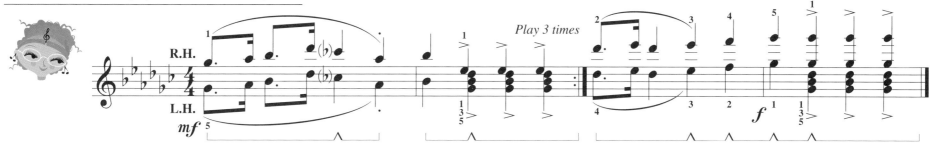

Tips from Katie: (pp. 38–39)

1. Can you believe who Katie brought to music night?
   Point to the notes as your teacher plays the song.

2. Circle the **repeated notes.**

3. Play *forte* on the LOWEST black-key groups.

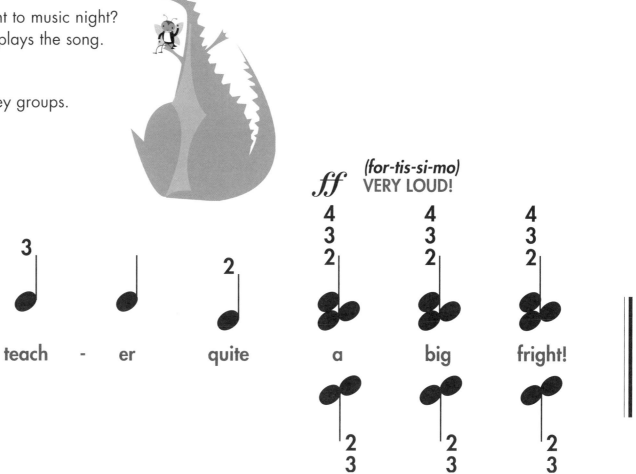

Paw Prints

Blocking Keys C-D-E

C D E

the 3-white keys just below the 2-black keys

For Left Hand

1. Begin in the MIDDLE of the piano.

2. To play a L.H. paw print, bring **fingertips 4-3-2** together. Play **C-D-E** keys at the same time.

2
3
4

3. Make a rainbow and play a "paw print" on each LOWER C-D-E group going down the keyboard.

For Right Hand

1. Begin in the MIDDLE of the piano.

2. To play a R.H. paw print, bring **fingertips 2-3-4** together. Play **C-D-E** keys at the same time.

4
3
2

3. Make a rainbow and play a "paw print" on each HIGHER C-D-E group going up the keyboard.

Where Is the Wabbit?
Finding C-D-E Keys

Dallas has lost his "wabbit."

1. Your teacher will say the rhyme and point to a keyboard.

2. Play and name the key where the "wabbit" has landed.

Alaka ZOOM, Alaka ZAM! The wabbit is lost! Where did he land?

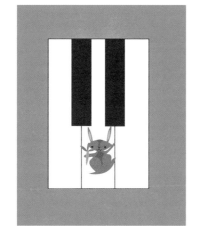

✏️ | WRITING BOOK **27**

Little Lost Kitty

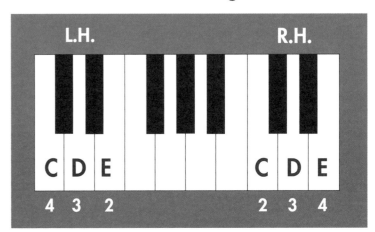

Quarter-Note Song on C-D-E

Tips from Millie and Marta:

1. Point to each note, counting "1, 1, 1, 1."
   Use **L.H.** for *down*-stems and **R.H.** for *up*-stems.

2. Guide your teacher! Point to each note and say
   the **finger number** as your teacher plays.

3. Circle all the **repeated notes**.

4. Play on the piano, singing the finger numbers.
   Can you see your "stone"? (See p. 12)

Words by Crystal Bowman

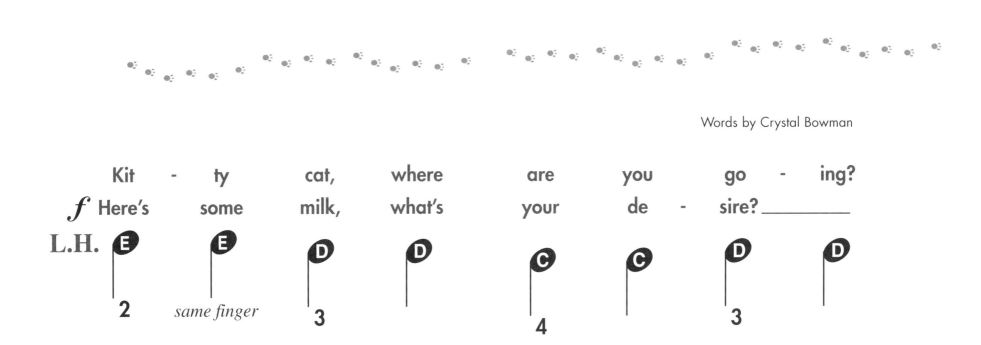

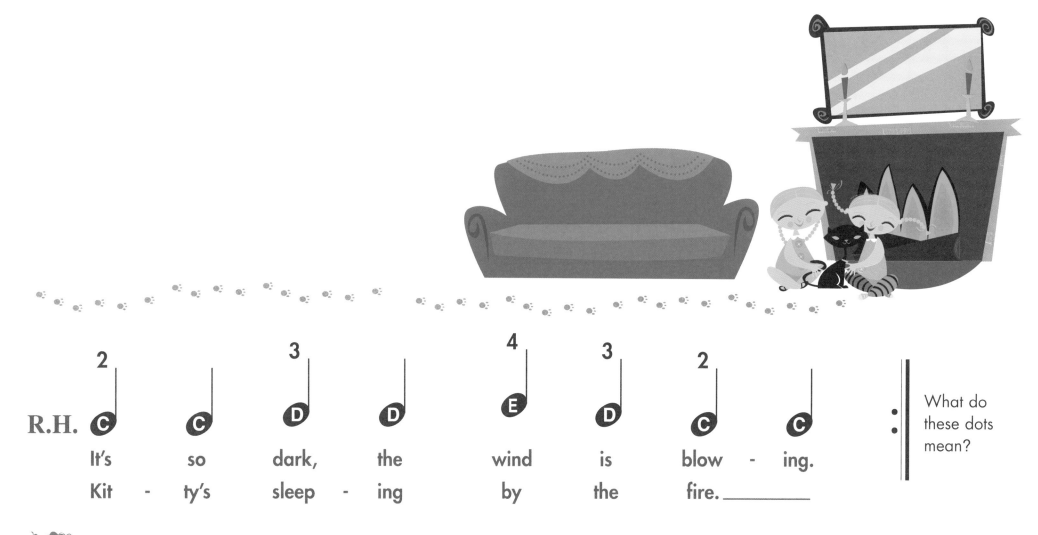

R.H.   **2** C   C   **3** D   D   **4** E   **3** D   **2** C   C

It's   so   dark,   the   wind   is   blow - ing.

Kit - ty's   sleep - ing   by   the   fire. _____

What do these dots mean?

Teacher Duet: (Student plays in the MIDDLE of the piano.)

rit. on repeat

Half Note = 2 Beats

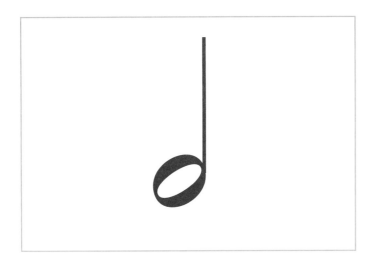

1. Say "half note" in a **forte** voice, **piano** voice, high voice, low voice.

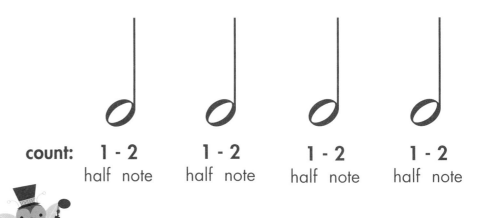

count: **1 - 2** **1 - 2** **1 - 2** **1 - 2**
half note half note half note half note

2. Tap and count aloud **forte**, then **piano**. Hold each note for 2 beats.

down-stem

L.H.

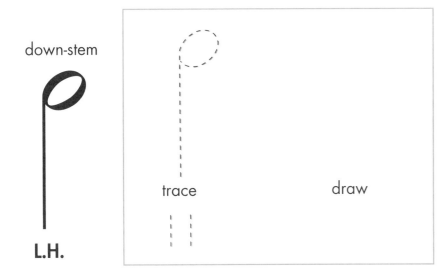

trace draw

3. Trace, then draw a half note for the **left hand**. Draw TWO slashes below to show **2 beats**.

up-stem

R.H.

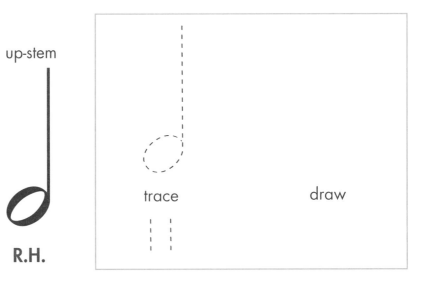

trace draw

4. Trace, then draw a half note for the **right hand**. Draw TWO slashes below to show **2 beats**.

Band Practice!

Tracking the Beat

1. Circle each R.H. rhythm in **RED**.
   Circle each L.H. rhythm in **BLUE**.

2. Play with the correct hand on **any key** using a **2-1 donut**.

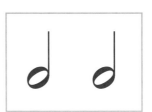

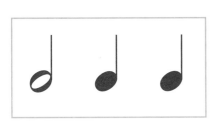

Keep a great steady beat!

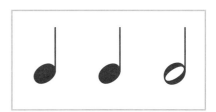

3. Your teacher will play a group of notes with the **left** or **right** hand. Point to the group you hear.

4. Have fun tapping ♩ and ♪ notes to *Turkey Talk* in your Writing Book, pp. 30–31.

23

Monsieur Mouse

(24)

C-D-E Melody with Half Notes

Tips from Monsieur Mouse:

1. Point to the notes, counting, "1, 1, 1-2."
   Use **L.H.** for *down*-stems and **R.H.** for *up*-stems.

2. Your teacher will help you circle every group of ♩ ♩ ♩ notes.

3. Play on the piano and sing the finger numbers or words.

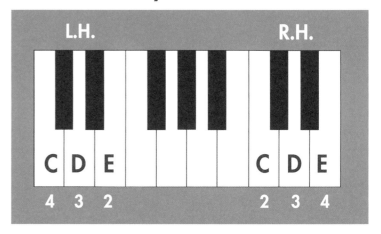

Words by Crystal Bowman

| Mon - sieur Mouse, | Mon - sieur Mouse | wel - comes friends | to his house. |
| Plays gui - tar, | sings a song. | His guests dance | all night long. |

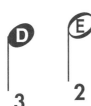

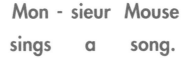
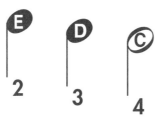

L.H. **C** **D** **Ⓔ** **Ⓔ** **D** **Ⓒ** **D** **D** **Ⓓ** **Ⓔ** **Ⓔ** **Ⓔ**
ƒ
4 3 2   2 3 4   3   2

Teacher Duet: (Student plays in the MIDDLE of the keyboard.)

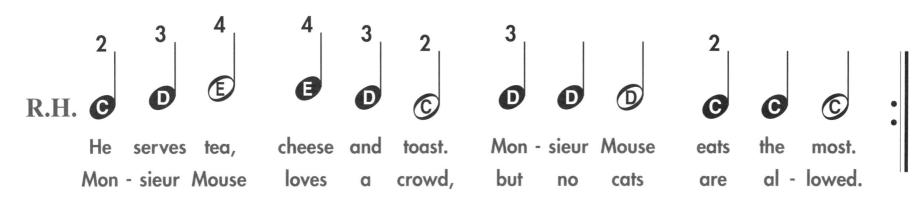

R.H.

2	3	4		4	3	2		3				2		
C	D	E		E	D	C		D	D	D		C	C	C

He serves tea,   cheese and toast.   Mon - sieur Mouse   eats the most.

Mon - sieur Mouse   loves a crowd,   but no cats   are al - lowed.

4. Have fun squeaking the sounds to *Mouse Rhythms* in your Writing Book, pp. 32–33.

25

♩ Can you find Tap?

Raccoon's Lullaby

Half-Note Song with Alternating Hands

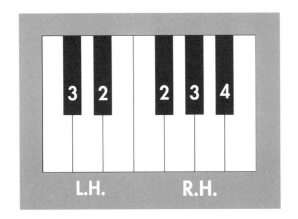

A lullaby is a song that helps someone go to sleep. Katie is singing to her favorite stuffed animal.

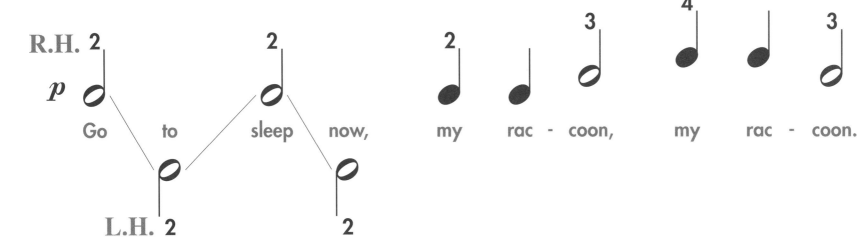

p

R.H. **2** | | **2** | | **2** | **3** | **4** | **3**
Go | to | sleep | now, | my | rac - coon, | my | rac - coon.

L.H. **2** | **2**

Teacher Duet: (Student plays HIGHER on the keyboard.)

✎ WRITING BOOK **34–35**

Tips from Katie: (pp. 48–49)

1. Point to each note, counting, "1-2, 1-2," etc.
   Use **L.H.** for *down*-stems and **R.H.** for *up*-stems.

2. Guide your teacher! Point to each note
   and say the **finger number** as your teacher plays.

3. Play on the piano, singing the finger numbers.
   Have fun singing with the CD!

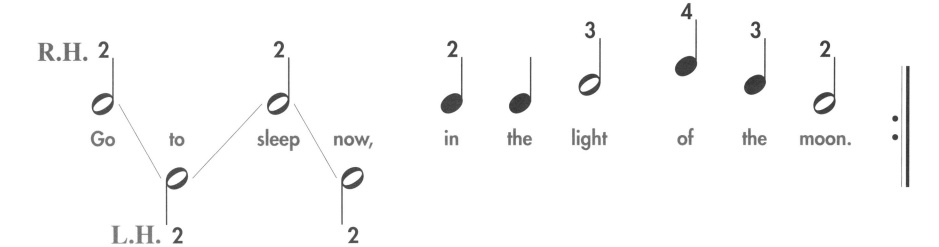

Go to sleep now, in the light of the moon.

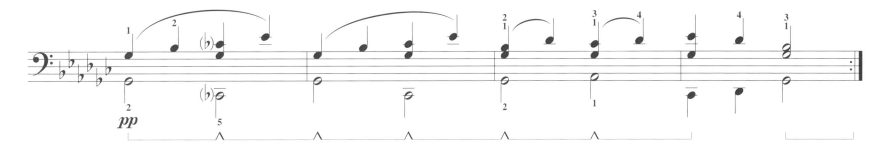

Bass Clef

The left hand uses the bass clef for LOW sounds.

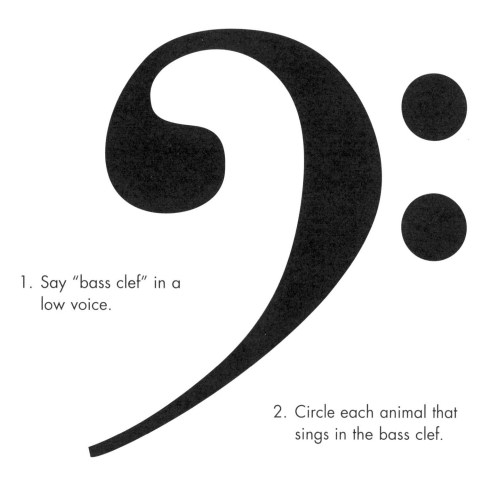

1. Say "bass clef" in a low voice.

2. Circle each animal that sings in the bass clef.

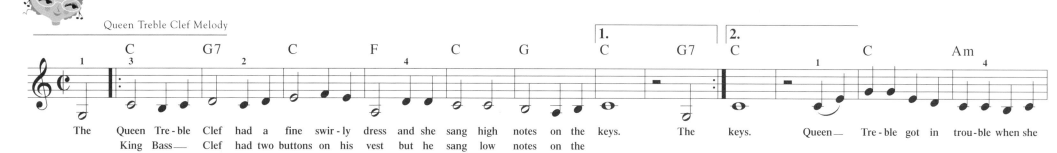

Queen Treble Clef Melody

The Queen Tre-ble Clef had a fine swir-ly dress and she sang high notes on the keys. The keys. Queen— Tre-ble got in trou-ble when she
King Bass— Clef had two buttons on his vest but he sang low notes on the

✏️ | WRITING BOOK 36–37

FF1619

Treble Clef

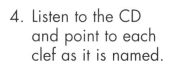

The right hand uses the treble clef for HIGH sounds.

1. Say "treble clef" in a high voice.

2. Circle each animal that sings in the treble clef.

3. Your teacher will play a **LOW** or **HIGH** sound. Quickly place R.H. or L.H. on the correct clef.

4. Listen to the CD and point to each clef as it is named.

went down to play on the keys that were real-ly rath-er low. But she jumped back nev-er to go a - gain where the bass clef notes go.

Mary's Rockin' Pets

28

C-D-E Melody with Half Notes

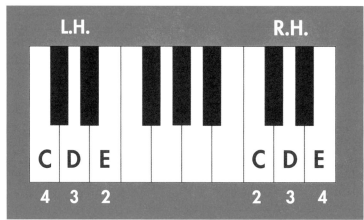

Tips from your friends:

1. As your teacher plays, point to each note and say the **letter name**.

2. Write f or p for the animal before each verse.

3. Play and sing the finger numbers, letter names, or words.

Traditional, words adapted

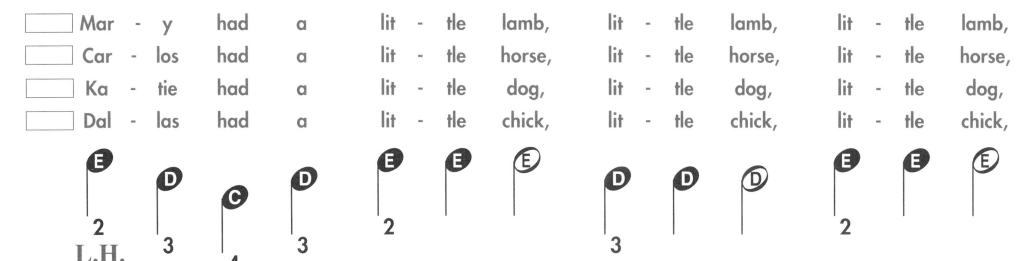

	Mar - y	had	a	lit - tle	lamb,	lit - tle	lamb,	lit - tle	lamb,
	Car - los	had	a	lit - tle	horse,	lit - tle	horse,	lit - tle	horse,
	Ka - tie	had	a	lit - tle	dog,	lit - tle	dog,	lit - tle	dog,
	Dal - las	had	a	lit - tle	chick,	lit - tle	chick,	lit - tle	chick,

Teacher Duet: (Student plays HIGHER on the keyboard.)

✎ | WRITING BOOK **38–39**

FF1619

R.H.

4	3	2	3	4			3		4	3	2	
E	D	C	D	E	E	E	D	D	E	D	C	C

Mar	-	y	had	a	lit	-	tle	lamb,	it	was	white	as	snow	-	flakes.
Car	-	los	had	a	lit	-	tle	horse,	it	was	brown	as	choc	-	'late.
Ka	-	tie	had	a	lit	-	tle	dog,	it	was	black	as	mid	-	night.
Dal	-	las	had	a	lit	-	tle	chick,	it	was	bright	as	sun	-	shine.

NEW! **GRAND STAFF GAMES**

Turn to p. 85 and do Mrs. Razzle-Dazzle's Game #1.

Teacher Note: These games will prepare students to read on the grand staff.

Whole Note = 4 beats

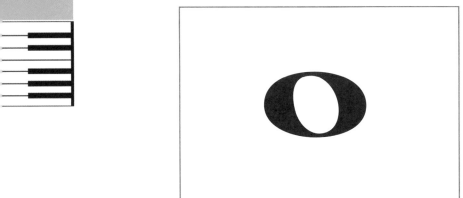

1. Say "whole note" in a **forte** voice,
   piano voice, high voice, low voice.

count: 1 - 2 - 3 - 4   1 - 2 - 3 - 4
whole - note - long - note   whole - note - long - note

2. Tap and count aloud **forte**, then **piano**.
   Hold each note for 4 beats.

3. Draw a whole note in each train car.
   Draw FOUR slashes in each car to show **4 beats**.

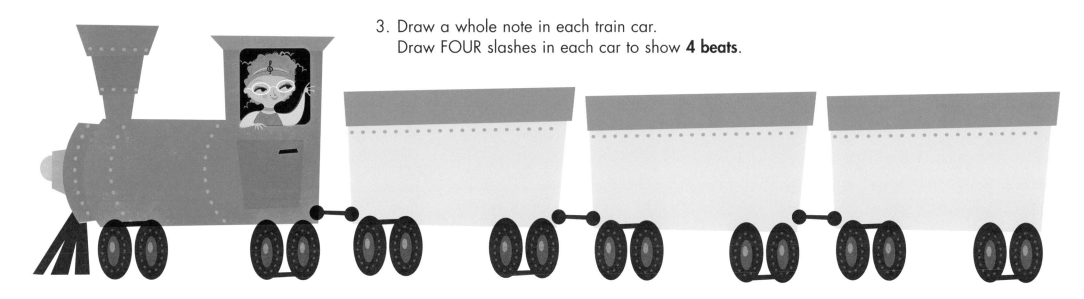

Train Rhythms
Tracking the Beat

1. Use a 3-1 donut and play each "train rhythm" on **C,** then **D,** then **E.** Count aloud!

2. Your teacher will play a box from each train on **C, D,** or **E.** Point to the rhythm you hear and name the key. Then you be the teacher!

Which hand plays?

_____

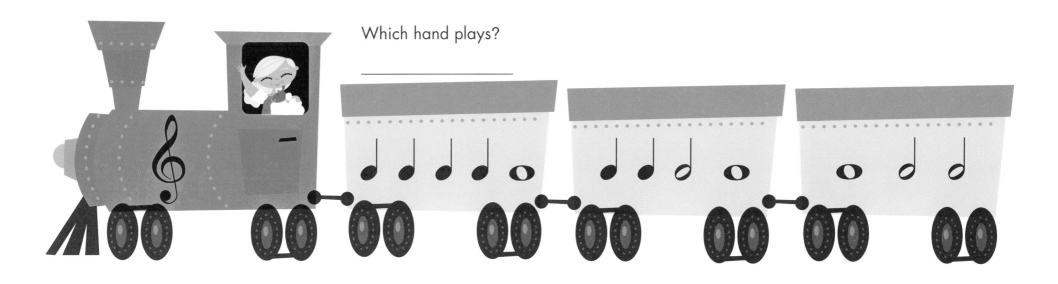

Which hand plays?

_____

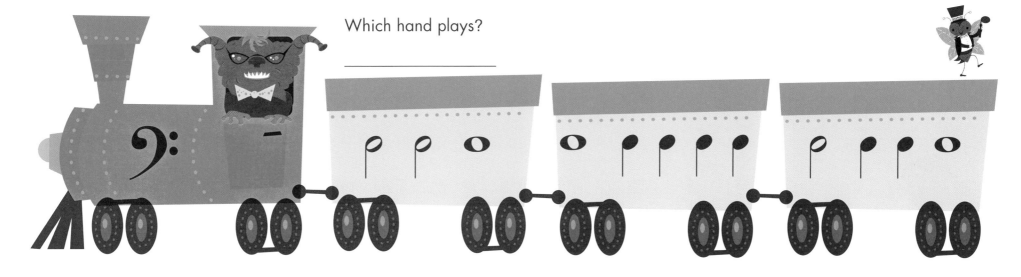

Old Pig-Donald

Black-Key Song with Whole Notes

R.H.

Old   Pig - Don - ald   had   a   song,
Played   his   key - board   all   day   long,

E - I - E - I - O! (2 - 3 - 4)

repeat!

L.H.

f

Teacher Duet: (Student plays HIGHER on the keyboard.)

R.H.

L.H.   *mf*   *p*

Tips from the farm: (pp. 56–57)

1. Guide your teacher! Point to the notes as your teacher plays the piece.

2. Play on the piano, singing the finger numbers or words.

3. After playing the duet, make up your own farm music. Use only **black keys.**
   When your teacher says, "Return to the farm!" play the first page again.

4. Have fun tapping *I Feel Rhythm* in your Writing Book, pp. 42–43.

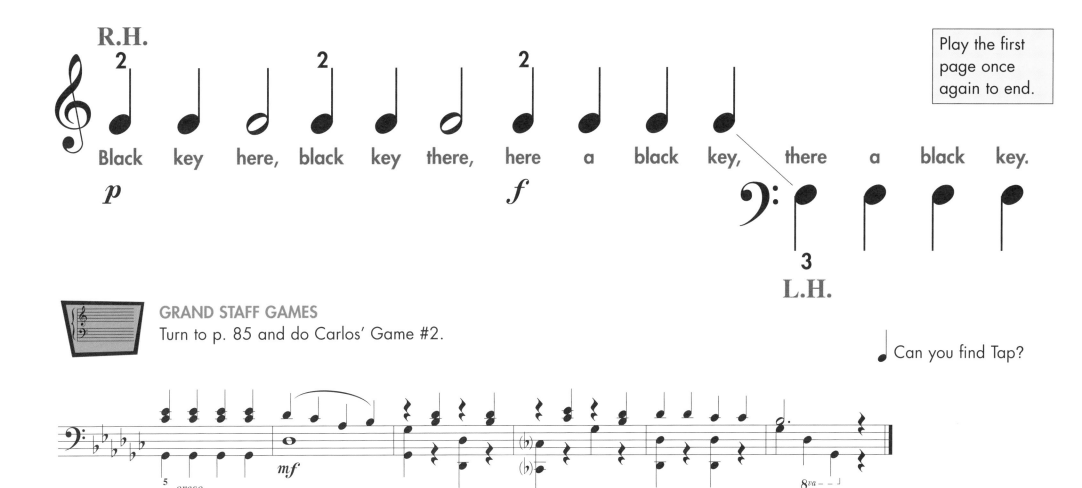

Black key here, black key there, here a black key, there a black key.

Play the first page once again to end.

GRAND STAFF GAMES
Turn to p. 85 and do Carlos' Game #2.

Can you find Tap?

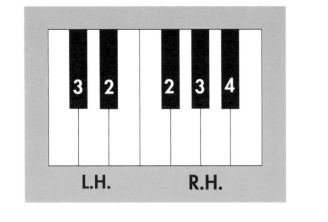

Shepherd, Count Your Sheep

32

Black-Key Song with Whole Notes

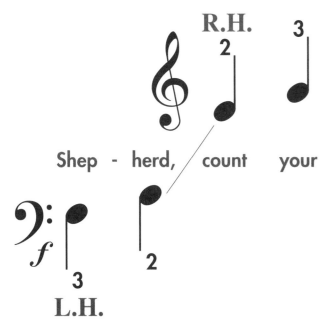

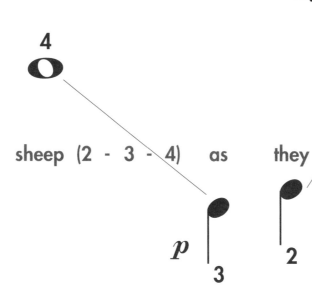

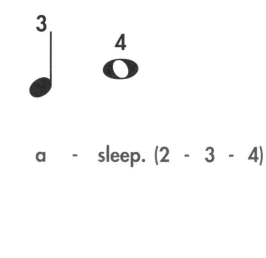

Shep - herd, count your sheep (2 - 3 - 4) as they fall a - sleep. (2 - 3 - 4)

Teacher Duet: (Student plays HIGHER on the keyboard.)

Tips from Carlos: (pp. 58–59)

1. Point to the notes as your teacher plays.
   Your teacher may ask you to count aloud.

2. Play on the piano and sing the finger numbers or words.
   Your teacher may press the pedal as you play.

3. Make up your own peaceful shepherd music. Play any black keys
   with the teacher duet. End softly on the highest black key.

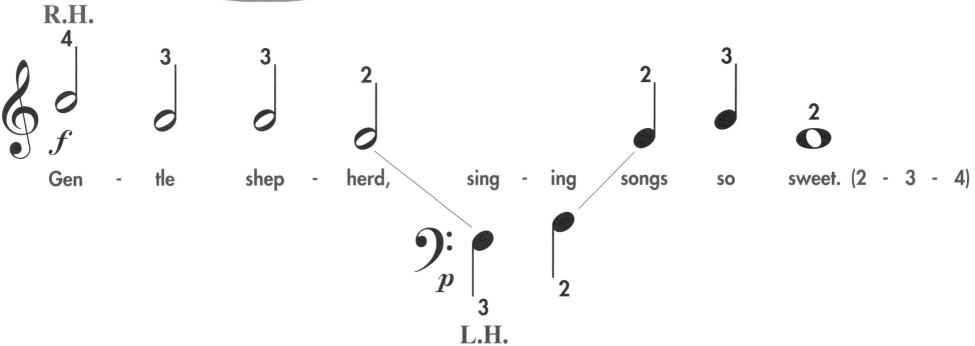

Gen - tle shep - herd, sing - ing songs so sweet. (2 - 3 - 4)

The Music Alphabet (33)

Exploring Alphabet Steps

1. Can you say or sing the entire alphabet for your teacher?

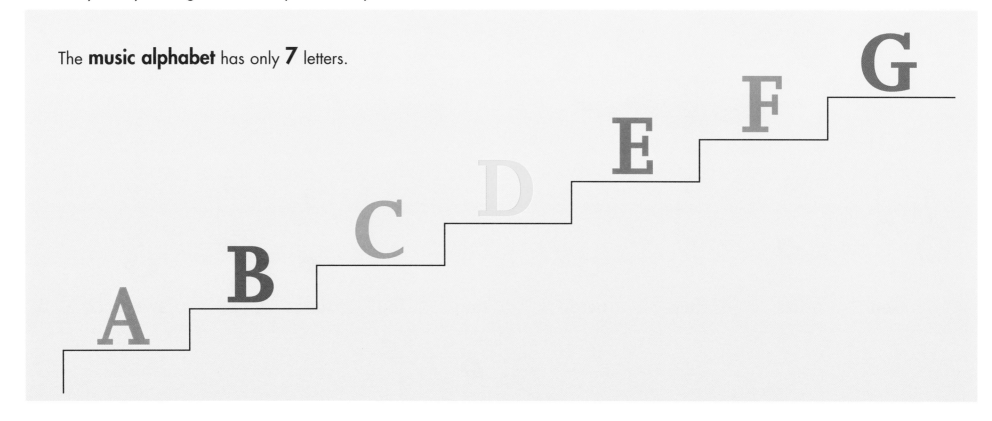

The **music alphabet** has only **7** letters.

2. Begin with **A**.

   Point to each letter and say it aloud.
   You are STEPPING UP the music alphabet.

3. Begin with **G**.

   Point to each letter and say it aloud.
   You are STEPPING DOWN the music alphabet.
   Sing the alphabet letters with the CD!

Cookie's Journey up the Mountain

34

1. Make a round cookie shape with **L.H. fingers 3 and 1.** Pretend you are carrying a cookie up a tall mountain (the keyboard).

2. Begin on the lowest key, **A.** Play and say the music alphabet going up the keyboard: **A B C D E F G.**

3. Stop on each **G** so that Dallas can "catch his breath."

4. At the MIDDLE of the keyboard, pass the "3-1 cookie" over to the R.H. Carry the cookie to the top of the piano. Keep saying the music alphabet aloud as you climb.

5. End on **C** for cookie! Pretend to eat your cookie. What flavor is it?

FF1619 WRITING BOOK **47** **61**

Tips from Carlos:

1. The *Here Comes the Bride* music must play **7 times** for the baboon bride to reach the groom.

2. After playing this song, try *Rockin' on C and F* with the CD. You and your teacher make up rockin' rhythms on any **C** and **F** keys with the music. Use **finger 3's** as in this song.

Jungle Wedding

Technique: C and F across the Keyboard

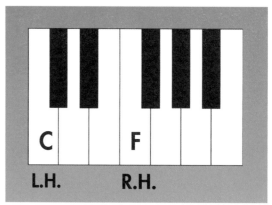

The 2-black keys help you find **C**.

The 3-black keys help you find **F**.

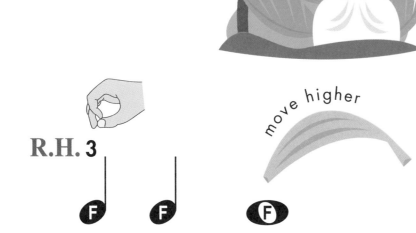

R.H. 3

F Here

F comes

F the

F bride!

move higher

L.H.

C

3

𝆑

Start on the LOWEST **C** and **F**.

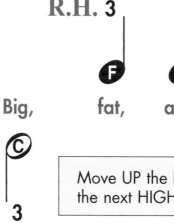

L.H.

C

3

Big,

R.H. 3

F fat,

F and

F wide!

Keep going higher!

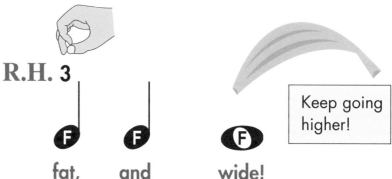

Move UP the keyboard to the next HIGHER **C** and **F**.

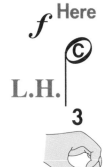

FF1619

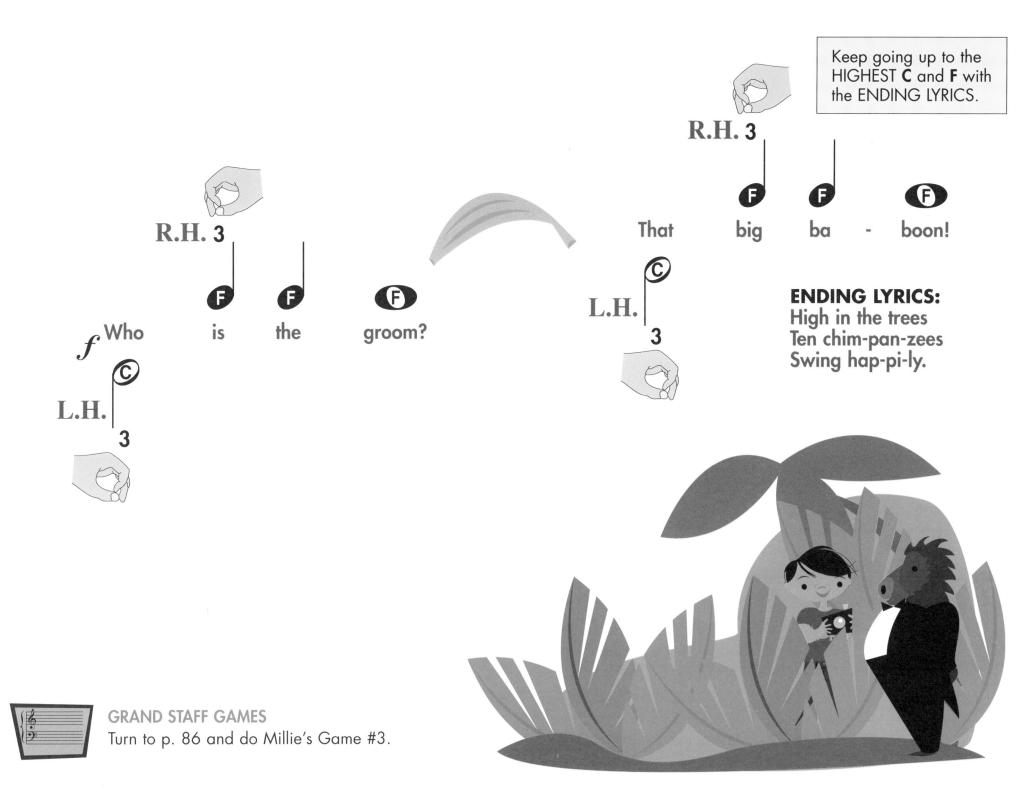

Keep going up to the HIGHEST **C** and **F** with the ENDING LYRICS.

R.H. 3

F **F** **F**

That big ba - boon!

R.H. 3

F **F** **F**

Who is the groom?

𝆑 **C**

L.H.

3

C

L.H.

3

ENDING LYRICS:
High in the trees
Ten chim-pan-zees
Swing hap-pi-ly.

GRAND STAFF GAMES
Turn to p. 86 and do Millie's Game #3.

Riding the Escalator

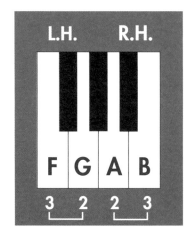

L.H.   **R.H.**

F G A B

3 2 2 3

the 4-white keys
just below the
3-black keys

Tips from your friends:

1. Pretend a group of friends are riding up the escalator.
   Your teacher will play and demonstrate a smooth ride.
   (Note: The student may move the bench and stand to play.)

2. Have fun crossing the L.H. *over* as the R.H. is playing.
   This will give the friends a smooth ride!

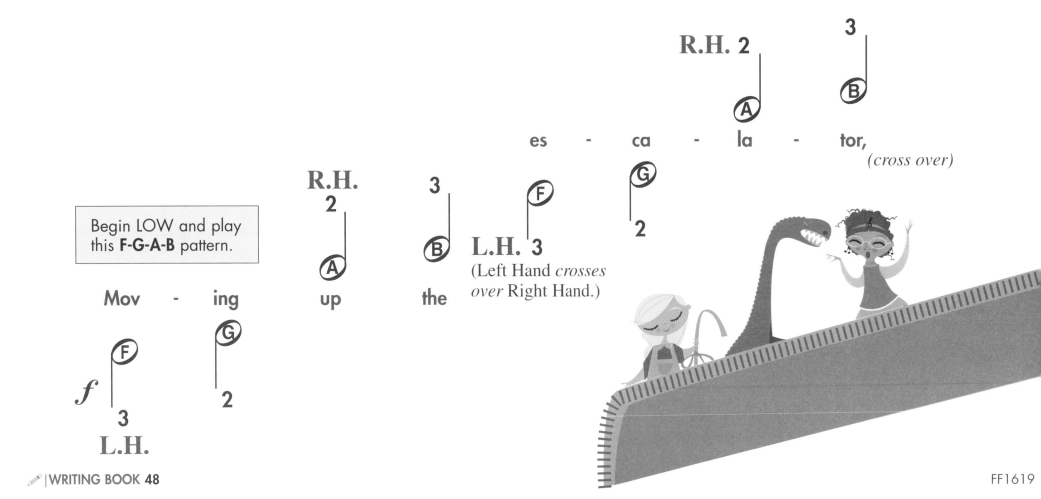

Begin LOW and play
this **F-G-A-B** pattern.

Mov - ing   up   the

R.H.
2
A

3
B

L.H. 3
(Left Hand *crosses*
over Right Hand.)

F
2

G
2

es - ca - la - tor,
(cross over)

R.H. 2
A

3
B

𝆑
F
3
L.H.

G
2

at the top just *(cross over)* sec - onds lat - er!

3. Have fun singing and doing the motions for *Hangin' on a Fencepost,* Writing Book, pp. 48–49.

Sneak-y Thumb

Technique: Playing the Thumb

1. There are four keyboards below. On the piano, "sneak" your **R.H. thumb** up to each key with a red letter. Follow the directions to the right.

2. Repeat with your **L.H. thumb**.

Teacher Duet for *Birthday Train*, p. 67: (Student plays HIGHER on the keyboard.)

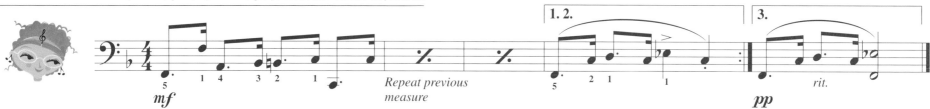

Directions for Sneak-y Thumb

Let your R.H. thumb reach out, with the rest of the fingers "hiding" in a loose fist.

On the piano, sneak the R.H. thumb up to **F** (for example).

Let the other fingers "come out" and rest on the keys. Notice your round hand!

FF1619

Birthday Train

Song using F-G-A-B

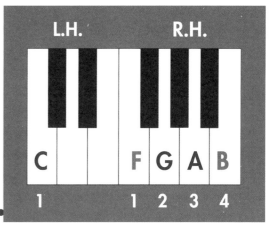

1. Find your new hand position. Hint! Sneak your thumbs up to **C** and **F**.

2. Play and sing finger numbers, letters, or words. Listen for the distant train whistle at the end!

F and **B** surround the **3-black keys.**
Play these together for a train whistle!

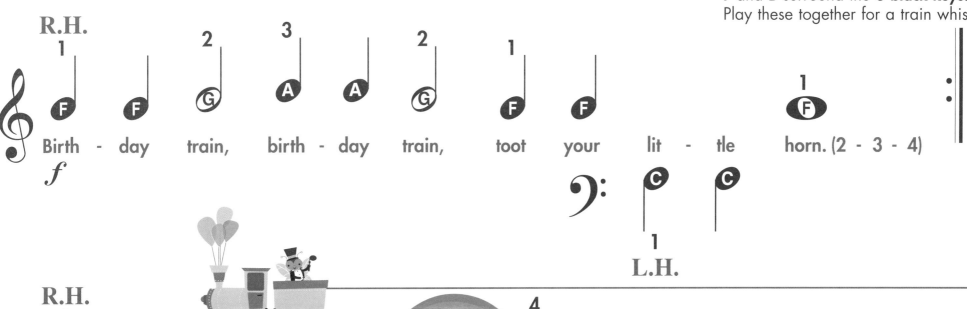

R.H.

1 — F — Birth -
  F — day
2 — G — train,
3 — A — birth -
  A — day
2 — G — train,
1 — F — toot
  F — your
  lit - tle
1 — F — horn. (2 - 3 - 4)

f

L.H.
C C
1

L.H.

R.H.

4
1 — B / F — TOOT!   *f*

B / F — TOOT!

B / F — TOOT!

4
1 — B / F — TOOT!   *p*

B / F — TOOT!

B / F — TOOT!

Move UP to the next HIGHER F-B.

Wish I Were a Fish

40

Song using F-G-A-B

Tips from Dallas:

1. Find your hand position. "Sneak" your thumbs up to **C** and **F.**

2. Play and sing finger numbers, letters, or words.

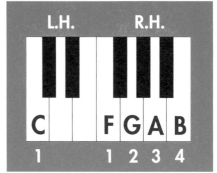

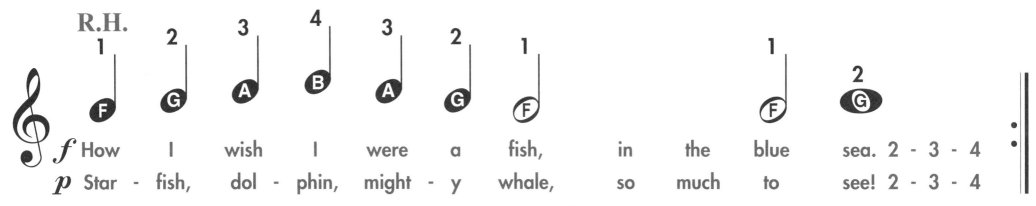

R.H.

1	2	3	4	3	2	1		1	2
F	G	A	B	A	G	F		F	G

f How   I   wish   I   were   a   fish,   in   the   blue   sea. 2 - 3 - 4

p Star - fish,   dol - phin,   might - y   whale,   so   much   to   see! 2 - 3 - 4

L.H.   1

Teacher Duet: (Student plays HIGHER on the keyboard.)

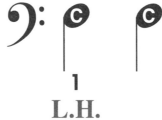

last time rit.

Fine   **9**   *D.C. al Fine*

R.H.   1 5 13

L.H.   5 1

mf - pp with pedal   *mf*

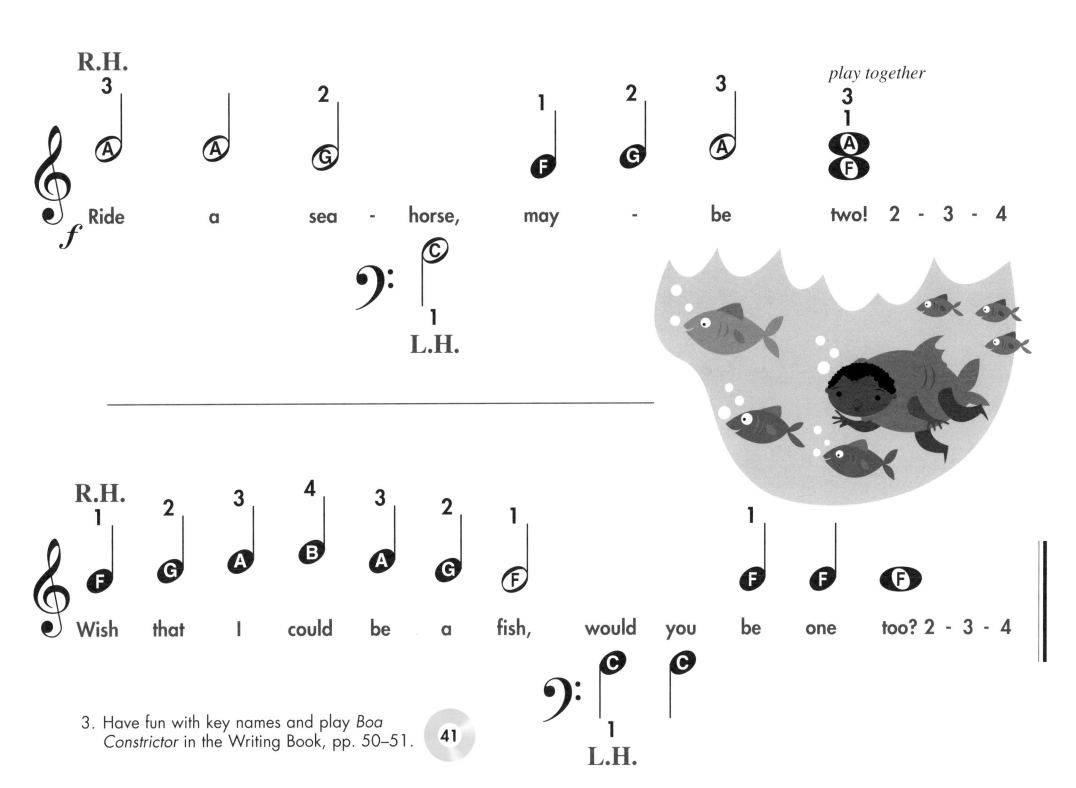

R.H.

f Ride a sea - horse, may - be two! 2 - 3 - 4

play together

L.H.

R.H.

Wish that I could be a fish, would you be one too? 2 - 3 - 4

L.H.

3. Have fun with key names and play *Boa Constrictor* in the Writing Book, pp. 50–51.

41

Oh! I Love Snack Time

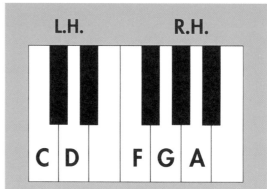

Technique: Firm Fingertips

Tips from Carlos and Katie:

1. Point to the notes and say the **letter names** as your teacher plays.

2. Find your hand position. Sing finger numbers and play on your fingertips!

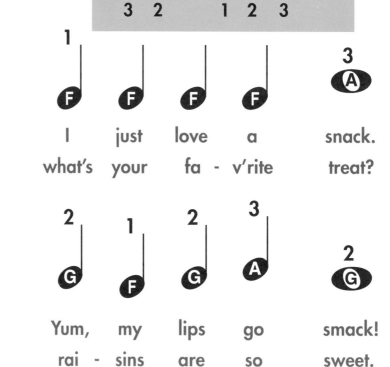

R.H.

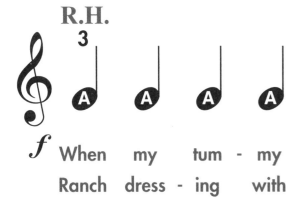

When   my   tum - my   starts   to   growl,   I   just   love   a   snack.
Ranch   dress - ing   with   car - rot   sticks,   what's   your   fa - v'rite   treat?

R.H.

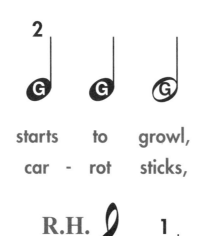

Cheese   and   crisp - y   crack - ers,   please,   Yum,   my   lips   go   smack!
Green   and   pur - ple   grapes   are   fun,   rai - sins   are   so   sweet.

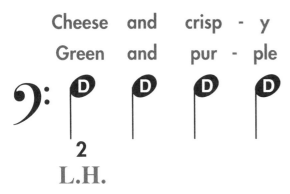

L.H.

FF1619

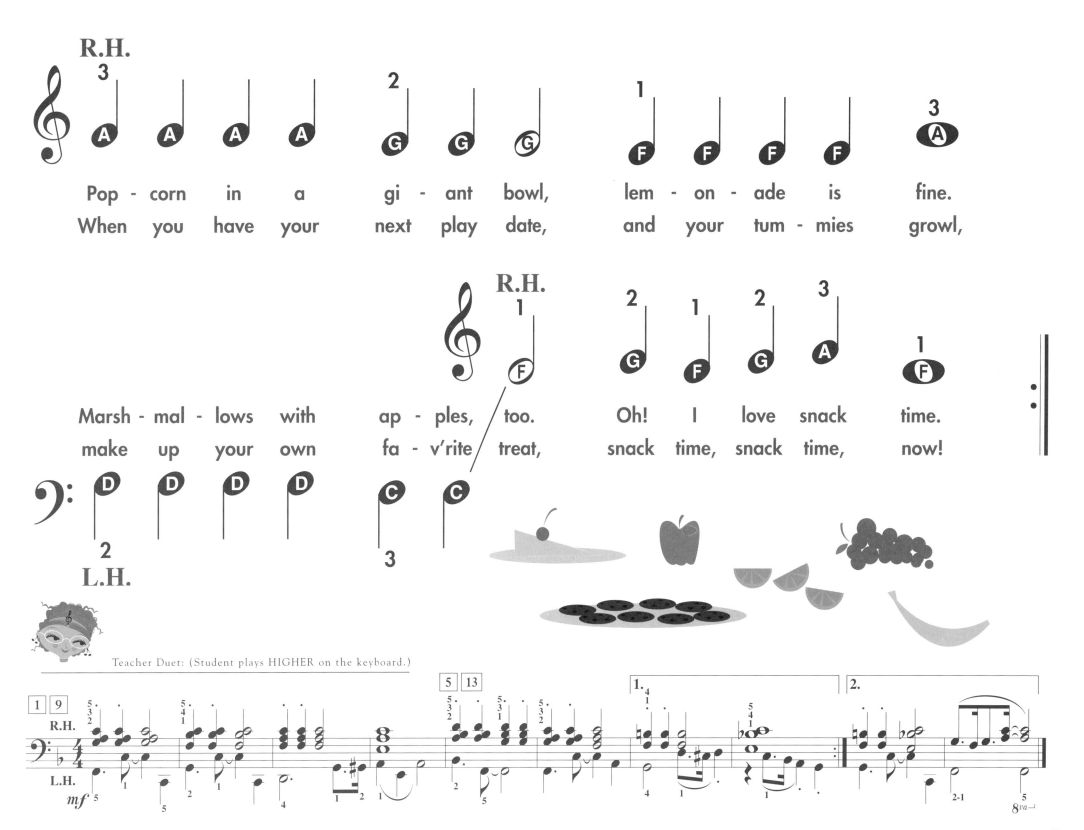

If You're Happy

Key-Name Review

Teacher Directions:

1. Student names each **key with a star** on p. 73.

2. Student practices finding each starred key quickly on the keyboard.

3. Play *If You're Happy* with the teacher part or CD. Student plays each key two times, as in the lyric.*

Teacher Piano Part

VERSE 1

If you're hap-py and you know it, play two C's. (C C) If you're hap-py and you know it, play two F's. (F F) If you're hap-py and you know it and you real-ly want to show it, if you're

hap-py and you know it, play two D's. (D D) If you're hap-py and you know it, play two E's. (E E) If you're hap-py and you know it, play two D's. (D D) If you're

VERSE 2

hap-py and you know it, and you real-ly want to show it, if you're hap-py and you know it, play two D's. (D D) If you're hap-py and you know it, play two G's. (G G) If you're

VERSE 3

hap-py and you know it, play two B's. (B B) If you're hap-py and you know it, and you real-ly want to show it, find two A's. Play them for-te on the keys! (A A)

*★★ = student

72   FF1619

Student Part

Verse 1:

If you're happy and you know it, play TWO

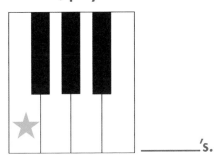

C_____'s.

If you're happy and you know it, play TWO

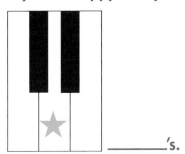

_____'s.

If you're happy and you know it, and you really want to show it, If you're happy and you know it, play TWO

_____'s.

Verse 2: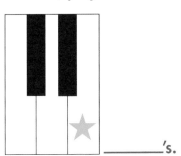

If you're happy and you know it, play TWO

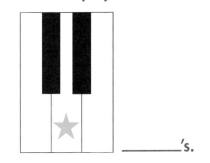

_____'s.

If you're happy and you know it, play TWO

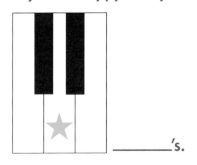

_____'s.

If you're happy and you know it, and you really want to show it, If you're happy and you know it, play TWO

_____'s.

Verse 3: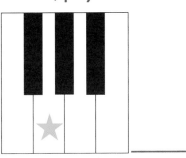

If you're happy and you know it, play TWO

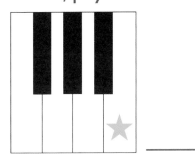

_____'s.

If you're happy and you know it, play TWO

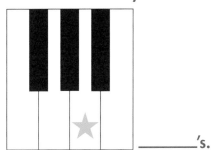

_____'s.

If you're happy and you know it, and you really want to show it, find TWO A's. Play them *forte* on the keys.

_____'s.

My L.H. C Scale (44)

Playing L.H. Fingers 5-4-3-2-1

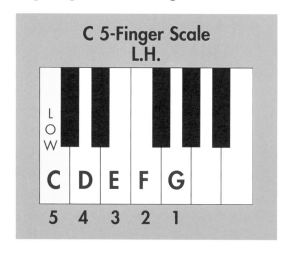

In music, a scale is like a ladder that steps UP or DOWN from one key to the next.

Begin on a LOWER C.

| This | is | my | C | scale. (2 - 3 - 4) | This | is | my | C | scale. (2 - 3 - 4) |
| C | D | E | F | G (2 - 3 - 4) | G | F | E | D | C (2 - 3 - 4) |

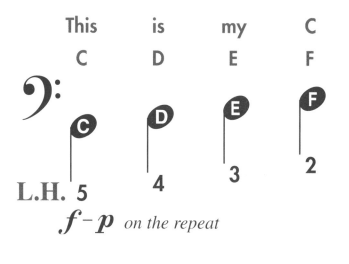

L.H. 5   4   3   2   G-1   G-1   2   3   4   5

f-p *on the repeat*

GRAND STAFF GAMES
Turn to p. 86 and do Marta's Game #4.

My R.H. C Scale
Playing R.H. Fingers 1-2-3-4-5

Tips from Mrs. Razzle-Dazzle: (pp. 74–75)

1. Do *Stone on the Mountain* with each hand as a warm-up (pp. 12–13).

2. On the closed keyboard cover, play and say the **finger numbers** for both hands.

3. Find the **C 5-finger scale** on the piano for each hand. Sing letter names or the words. Can you see your "stone"?

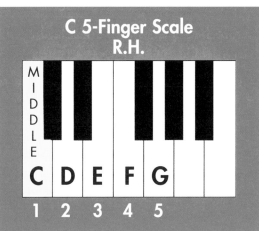

C 5-Finger Scale
R.H.

MIDDLE C D E F G
1 2 3 4 5

Begin on MIDDLE C.

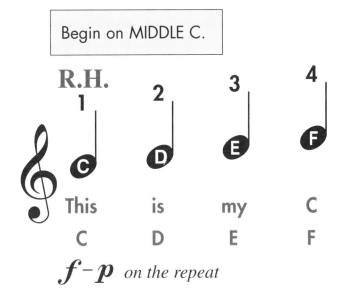

R.H.

1	2	3	4	5	5	4	3	2	1
C	D	E	F	G	G	F	E	D	C
This	is	my	C	scale. (2 - 3 - 4)	This	is	my	C	scale. (2 - 3 - 4)
C	D	E	F	G (2 - 3 - 4)	G	F	E	D	C (2 - 3 - 4)

f - p on the repeat

Teacher Duet: (Student plays HIGHER on the keyboard.) Use for pp. 74 and 75.

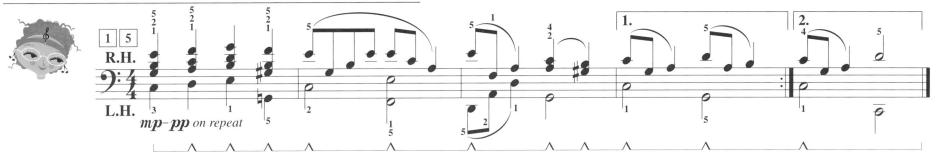

mp - pp on repeat

The Measure

Grouping Beats

In music, the notes are grouped into **measures**.
Think of a measure as a musical room.

Each measure has the same number of counts (beats).
Bar lines divide the music into measures.

Think of bar lines as the walls of the music room.

bar line   **bar line**

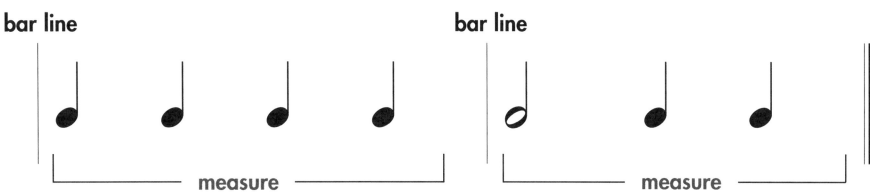

measure   measure

Review:
Double Bar Line
means the end.

one **thin** line
one **thick** line

Tips from Carlos :

1. Can you circle each **bar line** above?

2. How many beats are in each measure above?
   Circle a number in this blue box.

3. Turn to *Monsieur Mouse* on p. 46. Can
   you draw bar lines after every **4 beats**?

1   2   3   4

Katie's Dog Tucker

45

C 5-Finger Scale Song

Tips from Tucker:

1. Guide your teacher! Point to each note and say the **letter names** as your teacher plays.

2. Place your hands in the **C 5-finger scale**. Play, singing finger numbers, letter names, or words.

Words by Crystal Bowman

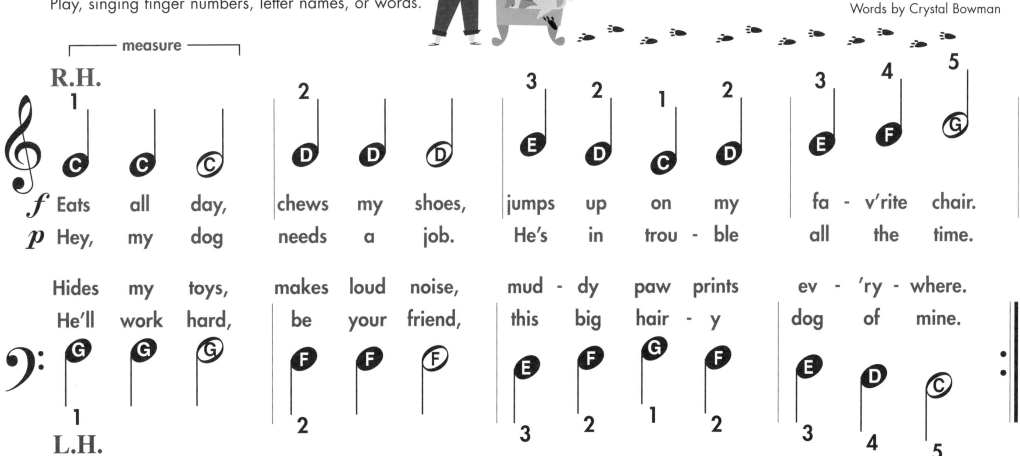

Teacher Duet: (Student plays HIGHER on the keyboard.)

Play two times, 2nd time *p*.

✎ | WRITING BOOK 55

Bed on a Boat

46

C 5-Finger Scale Song

Tips from Carlos:

1. Listen to your teacher play just the duet. Sway gently back and forth, as if you are rocking on a boat.

2. Guide your teacher! Point to each note saying the **letter name** as she/he plays the piece.

3. Play singing finger numbers, letter names, or words.

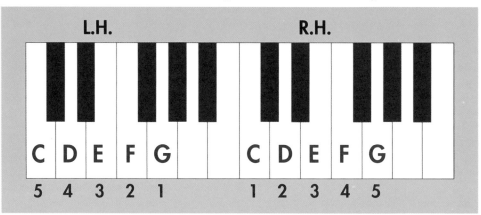

Words by Crystal Bowman

Wish my bed was on a boat. All night long I'd rock and float.

Won - der just what dreams I'd dream. Pi - rate ships and sub - ma - rines.

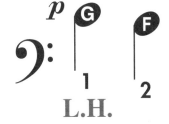 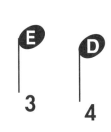 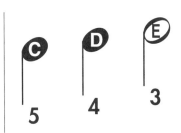 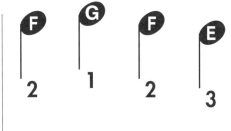 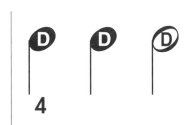

Teacher Duet: (Student plays HIGHER on the keyboard.)

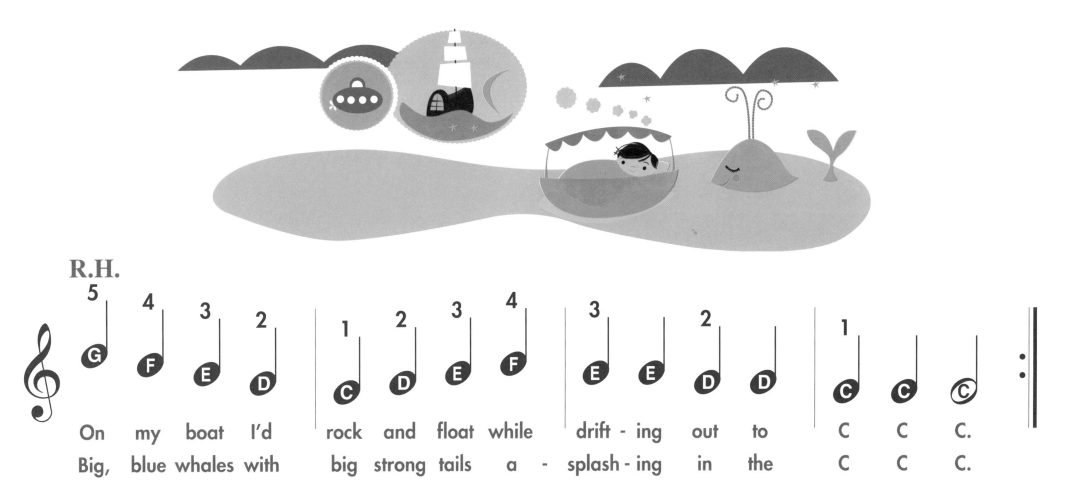

R.H.

5	4	3	2	1	2	3	4	3	2	1		
G	F	E	D	C	D	E	F	E E	D	D	C	C C

On my boat I'd | rock and float while | drift - ing out to | C C C.
Big, blue whales with | big strong tails a - | splash - ing in the | C C C.

GRAND STAFF GAMES
Turn to p. 86 and do Dallas' Game #5 and p. 87 for Katie's Game #6.

Use Tucker's Tips from p. 77.

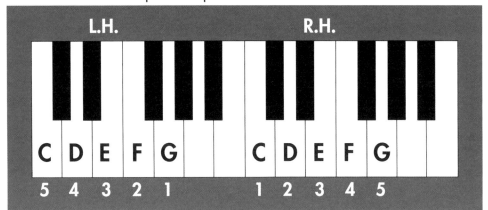

Eensie Weensie Spider

C 5-Finger Scale Song

R.H.

f Een - sie Ween - sie Spi - der climbed on Mid - dle C. (2 - 3 - 4)

Down came my hands, she jumped right down to E! (2 - 3 - 4)

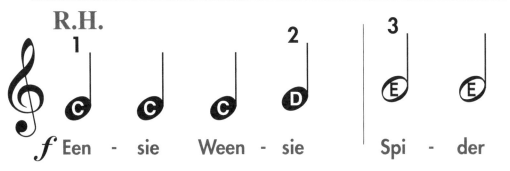

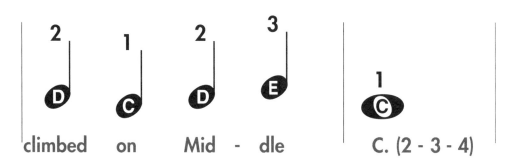

L.H.

Teacher Duet: (Student plays VERY HIGH on the keyboard.)

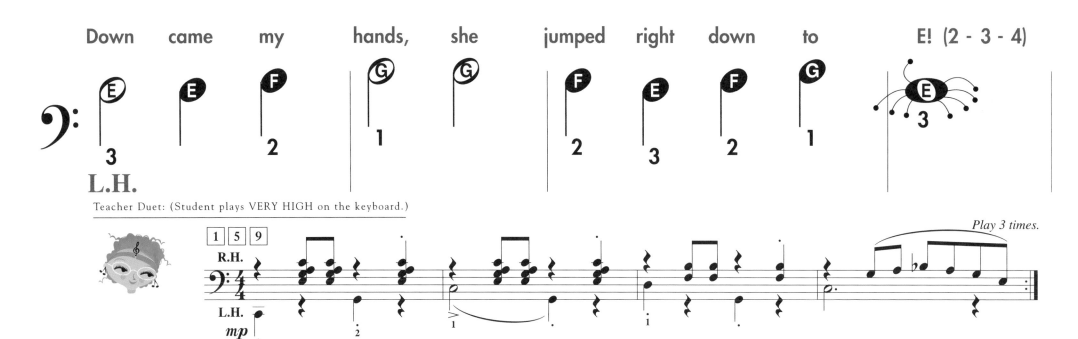

Play 3 times.

✎|WRITING BOOK 58–59 FF161

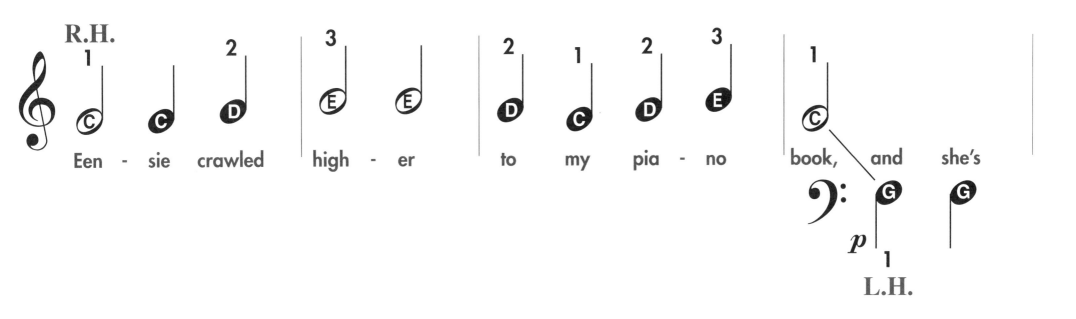

R.H.

1		2	3		2	1	2	3	1
C	C	D	E	E	D	C	D	E	C
Een	- sie	crawled	high	- er	to	my	pia	- no	book, and she's

L.H.
p G G
1

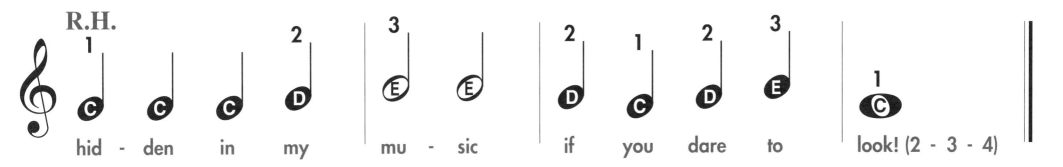

R.H.

1			2	3		2	1	2	3	1
C	C	C	D	E	E	D	C	D	E	C
hid	- den	in	my	mu	- sic	if	you	dare	to	look! (2 - 3 - 4)

GRAND STAFF GAMES
Turn to p. 87 and do Tucker's Game #7.

♩ Can you find the musical spider?

F1619

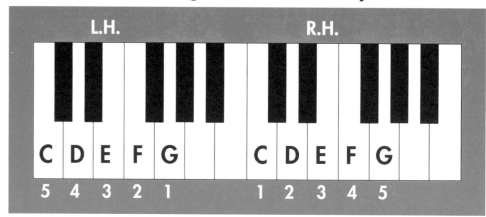

Graduation Party
C 5-Finger Scale Melody

(48)

Tips from your friends:

1. Guide your teacher! Point to each note and say the **letter name** as your teacher plays.

2. On the closed keyboard, play the song and say finger numbers.

3. Place your hands in the **C 5-finger scale**. Play and sing finger numbers, letter names, or words.

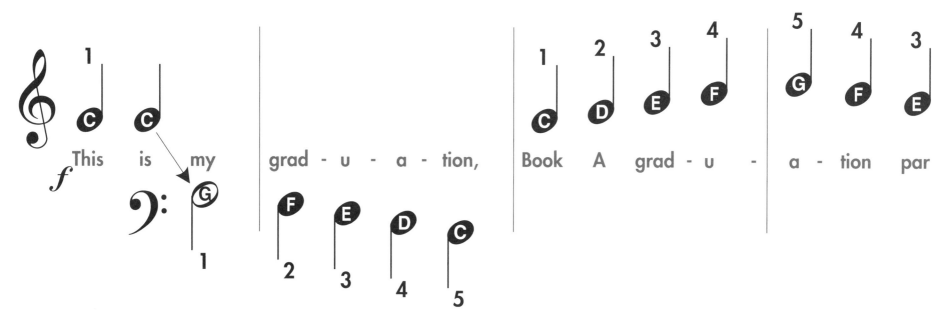

Teacher Duet: (Student plays HIGHER on the keyboard.)

✏ |WRITING BOOK 60–61   FF16

This is my grad - u - a - tion with my mu - sic friends. (2 - 3 - 4)

play **3** together

Hip, hip, hoo - ray! Hip, hip, hoo - ray!

GRAND STAFF GAMES
Turn to p. 87 and do Tap's Game #8.

Play any **LOW C** with finger 3 braced with the thumb.

Grand Staff Games

Piano music uses two staffs.

A staff has **5 lines** and **4 spaces**.

Together we call them the **GRAND STAFF.**

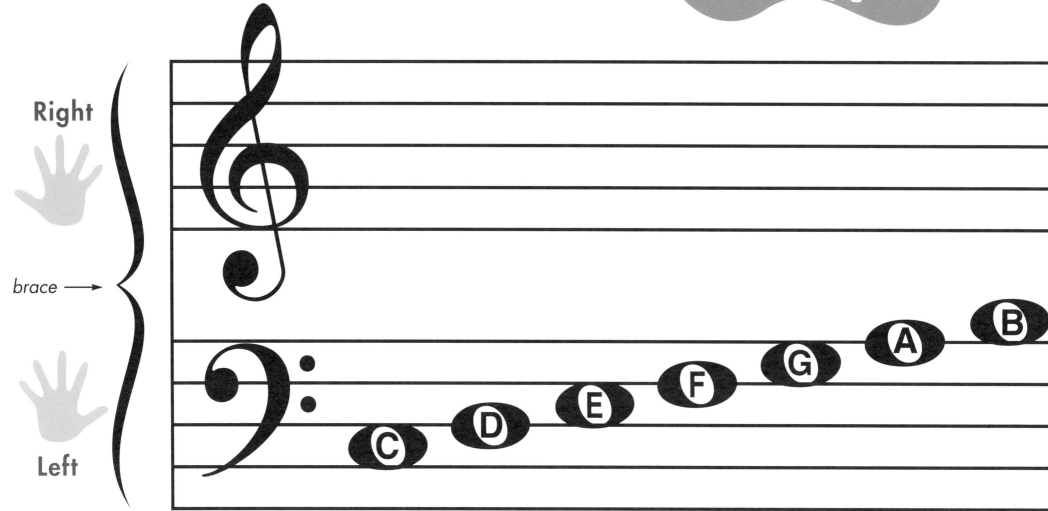

Right

brace →

Left

1. Mrs. Razzle-Dazzle's Game

Learn the word STAFF.

Count the **5 lines** and **4 spaces.**

Your teacher will point to a line.

Can you name the number?

2. Carlos' Game

Say the word GRAND STAFF.

Find and name the **treble** and **bass clef.**

Your teacher will play HIGH or LOW notes. Point to the 𝄞 with your **R.H.** or the 𝄢 with your **L.H.** for the sound.

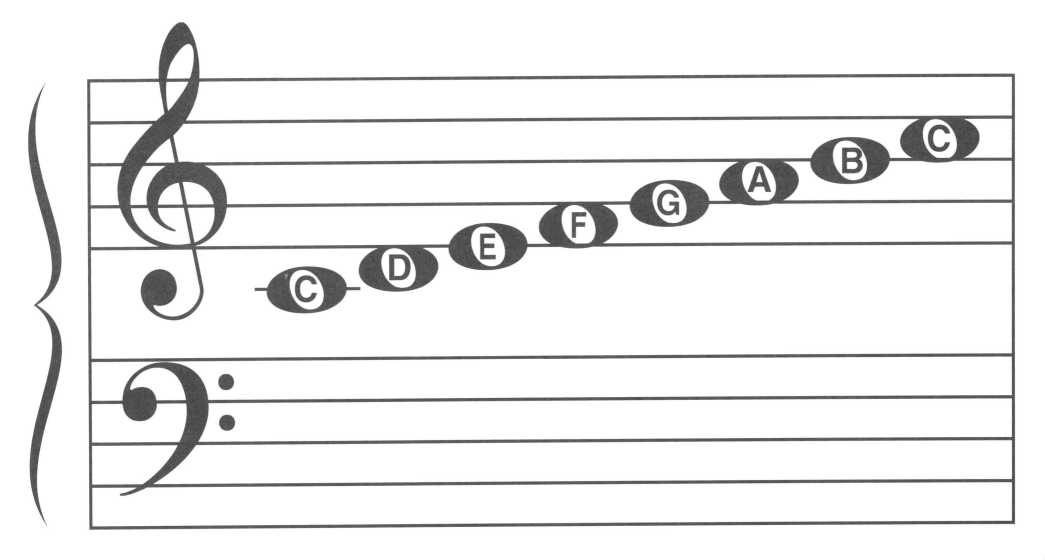

F1619

and more grand staff games . . .

3. Millie's Game

Notes can be written on a **line** or a **space.**

LINE	SPACE

Your teacher will point to a note on pp.84–85.

Say "line" or "space" for each note!

4. Marta's Game

Close your eyes.

Your teacher will cover a note with a dime!

Open your eyes and name the note **below** and **above** (before and after) the coin.

Now can you name the **covered note**? Is it a line or space note?

Remove the coin and check your answer!

5. Dallas' Game

On p. 84, play **Bass C–D–E–F–G** with your **L.H.** while pointing to the matching bass notes on the staff with your other hand. Say the notes aloud!

Now your teacher will choose and play a **Bass C, D, E, F,** or **G** key.

Name the key and point to the matching bass clef note on the staff.

6. Katie's Game

On p. 85, play **Middle C-D-E-F-G** with your **R.H.** while pointing to the matching treble notes on the staff with your other hand. Say the notes aloud!

Now your teacher will choose and play a **Middle C, D, E, F, or G** key.

Name the key and point to the matching treble note on the staff.

7. Tucker's Game

Put a dime over each **line note** for all the notes shown on the GRAND STAFF. (pp. 84–85)

Think the alphabet! Can you name each covered line note? Remove the dime to check your answer.

You may also like to try Tucker's Game with **space notes!**

8. Tap's Game

Listen to *Tigers at My Door* (p. 28) and point to the matching notes on the treble staff (p. 85)

Hint: C steps up to G, then G steps up to C.

You and your teacher may think up more games on your own!

Congratulations, my friend

_____

(Sign and join the club!)

**You have completed
My First Piano Adventure® Lesson Book A.
We can't wait to see you in Lesson Book B!**